CHILD HEALTH IN SOCIAL CONTEXT

Parental Employment and the Start of Secondary School

Julia Brannen and Pamela Storey

Acknowledgements

We wish to thank Paddy Walls for her considerable contribution to the research: Paddy helped to develop the interview schedule for the case studies and conducted most of the interviews with the children and their parents to a very tight timetable. We are also grateful to staff at Thomas Coram Research Unit for their administrative and computing support, especially Maria Harrison who helped with the manuscript. Finally, recognition needs to be given to the heads and staff of the schools participating in the study, to the parents who agreed to be interviewed, and, above all, to the children who made such excellent research participants.

Published by the Health Education Authority

ISBN 0 7521 0526 4

Health Education Authority
Hamilton House
Mabledon Place
London WC1H 9TX

Typeset by DP Photosetting, Aylesbury, Bucks
Printed in Great Britain

Contents

Foreword

This research report was commissioned, by the HEA, as part of a wider programme of research, to coincide with the United Nations' International Year of the Family in 1994. The research programme aimed to provide a greater insight into the mechanisms of family health, thus informing parents and professionals about effective ways of taking forward health promotion work with young people.

The Health Education Authority has a national remit for health education in England. It advises the Secretary of State, organises national health education campaigns and works with health service commissioners and providers to help them implement national health promotion targets. Good research based evidence is key to improving health and healthcare, and for this reason the HEA bases its campaigns on thorough needs assessment and evaluation.

Over the last decade the HEA has worked with parents and professionals to improve and promote the health of children. Emphasis is put on offering appropriate support to parents in the complex and sometimes stressful task of promoting the health and education of children and young people. Projects have focused on increasing the uptake of child immunisations, reduction of child accidents, advice and support for pregnant mothers and first time parents. We have also produced training materials for those working in parenting education and initiated inter-agency collaboration through workshops, seminars and the provision of resource databases. The research reported on here forms part of the on-going needs assessment in the area of parent and child health. Previous initiatives include a report on health promotion for children under five, and a review of the literature assessing the effectiveness of health promotion interventions on infant mortality and morbidity.

The HEA encounters a constant demand from health professionals to provide materials to support parents, yet appropriate health education messages, and the style and manner in which they are relayed, are increasingly open to question. This report highlights the importance of recognising the environmental, social and economic constraints which influence parental behaviour and shows how parental roles and needs change as children grow and develop. It also stresses that there is no 'blueprint' defining the ideal parent. Different parents adopt different parenting styles which may work to equal effect; individual styles need to be respected and supported. Such messages are particularly important in an environment where parents are probably under more intense pressure, from the media and a range of professionals, than at any other time, to create a healthy, nurturing and moral environment for their young.

A full list of publications forming part of the HEA Family Health Research series may be found at the end of the report.

Kathy Elliott

Executive summary

Children's health and health-related behaviour are influenced by social context. This study examines the health and health-related behaviour of children entering secondary school in the context of:

- parental employment patterns, particularly of mothers
- household relations between parents and children
- gender, ethnic origin and household structure.

MOTHERS' EMPLOYMENT AND CHILDREN'S HEALTH-RELATED BEHAVIOUR

- Two-thirds of children starting secondary school are likely to have a mother in employment, split equally between those in full-time and those in part-time employment, especially in two-parent households. Where mothers in single-parent households are employed, they are likely to be employed full-time. Moreover, many mothers are considering increasing their labour market involvement at this time. Full-time employment rates are highest among mothers of children who are the youngest in the household.

- However, despite high employment rates, three-quarters of children have one or both parents at home after school, with children of full-time employed parents (in both single- and two-parent households) most likely to spend time at home alone after school.

- Children's diet is related to their mothers' employment, with those whose mothers work full-time more likely to take a packed lunch to school, a practice associated with a higher intake of brown bread, fruit and vegetables. Moreover, boys, but not girls, whose mothers work full-time, consume chips, crisps, biscuits and fizzy drinks, etc. significantly less often than those whose mothers are part-time employed or not employed.

- Children's access to information concerning puberty is influenced by mothers' employment, with full-time employed mothers more likely than part-time employed and non-employed mothers to talk about menstruation to their daughters.

- While parental smoking is related to their employment status (rates are highest among unemployed fathers and lowest where both parents in the household are working full-time), children's smoking is related to parental employment status *and* parental smoking habits. Paradoxically, daughters of full-time employed mothers are less likely to have tried smoking than daughters of part-time or non-employed mothers if their mothers smoke, and are significantly more likely to smoke if their employed mothers are non-smokers.

- Children whose mothers are employed are less likely to have time off school for sickness than those whose mothers are not employed. Those children whose mothers work full-time are more likely to have responsibility for looking after themselves at home when they are ill although mothers are still the most common carers whatever their employment status. Fathers' involvement is not affected by mothers' employment status and they care for sick children in only 5 per cent of cases. According to the case study accounts of working mothers, mothers adopt a variety of strategies when children are ill: leaving children alone for part of the time, taking time off part of the time, working at or from home, and taking children to their workplaces. Mothers' decisions about how much responsibility to accord their children when they are ill are the outcomes of employers' attitudes, practices and geographical proximity as well as mothers' judgements concerning symptoms, diagnosis and hence the 'appropriateness' of leaving their children on their own when they are ill.

HOUSEHOLD NEGOTIATIONS AND CHILDREN'S HEALTH AND HEALTH-RELATED BEHAVIOUR

- Parents' perceptions of *children's health* and *lifestyles* and *body image* are rosier than those of children who paint a mixed picture. One-half of 12-year-olds rate their health as only 'fairly good', one-third say their lifestyle is 'healthy and unhealthy', one-half of girls (a third of boys) are unhappy or ambivalent about their body shape and size, and less than half rate their diet as 'healthy'.

- Children's entry to secondary school is marked by increased responsibility in particular for *food decisions* at school, a practice which limits children's access to a healthy diet. In some cases children purchase all the food and drink they consume in the school day from the school cafeteria which tends toward the 'junk' end of the food continuum. Eating in the school cafeteria is, moreover, associated with lower scores on brown bread, fresh fruit and vegetables compared with taking packed lunch. Some parents justify this practice as an educational device which facilitates the process of growing up. In other cases parents provide children with a packed lunch and thereby endeavour to control children's food intake. Some children prefer packed lunch, regarding the cafeteria as providing choices between unhealthy options. In other cases, parents and children adopt a compromise with children negotiating money for a cafeteria lunch on one or two days a week which they consider a treat. Parents often find it difficult to find out what children eat in the school cafeteria.

- Household discussion of *sex* and *puberty* involving children and, more often than not, mothers takes a variety of forms:

  Non-discursive households, where sex information is provided outside the household (by teachers), usually because of cultural taboos, a practice which is common among Asian-origin households.

  Potentially discursive households, from a variety of origins, in which children are considered not yet sufficiently emotionally or biologically developed to require sex education or where instruction is thought to be provided by others in the household (by the other parent or older siblings).

  Discursive households, which fall along a continuum, ranging from a 'jigsaw approach' in which a parent gives bits of information, to full explanations about sex which are typically provided by lone mothers.

- Households adopt a number of different approaches in response to *smoking*.

  Parents are proactive in banning smoking and in preventing children from taking it up, especially those of Asian origin. This approach is not always successful and where it is unsuccessful may give way to another approach.

Children (rather than parents) are proactive in discouraging smoking at home. Parents and children in some households take a liberal view either on the grounds that children's experimentation is a normal part of growing up (a parental view), or on the grounds that prescription has effects counter to those desired, a view favoured by children and adults.

These approaches suggest that both children and parents have absorbed health messages linking smoking with ill health. However, Asian origin parents tend to regard smoking as infringing moral rather than health norms; in particular they expect members of younger generations in their families to show 'respect' for older generations by refraining from smoking in front of them. In general, children, by contrast with parents, focus on the unaesthetic aspects of smoking, namely the nasty smell associated with the habit, and regard smoking as incompatible with playing sports.

Both parents and children are sceptical about the effects of anti-smoking education. Smoking is seen as a personal choice or an individual decision made, according to children's accounts, in order to impress their friends and assumed by boys in particular to give them a 'hard' image.

- While mothers are the principal persons to decide if children should stay away from school because of *illness*, children are actively involved in these negotiations. At the start of secondary school, children make illness claims which may or may not be legitimate in their own terms or those of their parents. Children are highly attuned to the distinctions between legitimate and non-legitimate reasons for staying off school, with some emphasising the trust that their mothers have in them and others complaining that their claims are not taken seriously. In some instances children themselves admit to feigning illness in the context of having problems at school. Parents note a significant amount of illness in children's first year at secondary school.

Mothers try to balance the needs of their sick children for care against other demands on their time. The issue is especially significant for employed mothers. The fact that few children look after themselves is reflected in the variety of strategies mothers adopt with respect to their care which do not necessarily mean mothers taking all the time off work. Some adopt flexible strategies such as leaving their children alone for part of the time, taking time off for part of the time, and/or working from home some of the time. A few mothers are employed in workplaces which allow or are sympathetic to mothers bringing their children into work on odd occasions.

IMPLICATIONS FOR HEALTH INTERVENTION

- The study suggests that health-related behaviour and health strategies are negotiated at household level involving parents and in some instances siblings. They are also affected by life-course transitions, including those of children, such as moving to a new level of the education system. Health education curricula need to take account of the varying social characteristics of children – parental employment, household composition, sex and ethnic origin, together with the changing life-course and different contexts children experience:

– the significance of children's *gender* for health priorities such as the importance of a slim body image for girls and a 'hard' image for boys, and for attitudes towards communication, for example boys express less inclination to disclose and discuss personal matters.

– the significance of *ethnic* origin for the discussion of health issues which raise cultural taboos and concerns, for example the difficulties of providing sex education in Asian-origin families while the issue of smoking is proscribed out of respect for elders rather than for health reasons.

– the significance of *western ideas of individual development* and freedom may work against enforcing strict rules concerning the prohibition of smoking. These ideas may conflict with the strong 'anti' messages of health education with respect also to the use of other drugs. Notions of personal choice and responsibility are central to dietary behaviour even though mainly unhealthy food options are provided in schools' cafeteria. They are also central to child-rearing beliefs and practice but may have less credence among parents from non-western societies. They may conflict with their concerns about keeping their children safe, especially girls whom they seek to protect for gender-related cultural reasons also, from a hostile and dangerous external environment. By contrast western-origin parents may consider it important for their children to learn to negotiate the external world and therefore give children more freedom to do so.

– the significance of *household structure* and composition, for example the assumption of responsibility by lone mothers for sex education in the absence of resident fathers and the danger in two-parent households of assuming that such matters will be covered by the other parent.

– the overarching assumption that health education should be presented from an *adult perspective*. For example, while many parents are clear that, as children, they were not happy with their parents' approach to sex education, they repeat these mistakes or omissions with their own children. Parents seek to find the 'right moment' to impart information when children continue to find talking to parents embarrassing, or they provide only partial information without giving the very basic factual 'nuts and bolts' of sex. Adults rarely ask children what they want in terms of information or mode of communication.

SUGGESTIONS FOR FURTHER RESEARCH

• Further research should take on board children's perspectives on health and how these are influenced in different social contexts and situations – peer groups, wider kin groups, the classroom situation – and how these different perspectives are negotiated and change across contexts. It should consider how children's health beliefs and representations, as well as their health-related behaviour, are influenced by adult/child relationships and child/child relationships and in relation to group dynamics, for example larger versus smaller groups and individual versus dyadic contexts.

• Specific studies need to be devoted to children's health in the context of their use of the wider, unsupervised environment, namely the built environment, including the street, shopping centres and neighbourhoods and different forms of transport. Children's mortality from accidents fell between 1969 and 1990 for all age groups except in the 10–14 age group (Woodroffe *et al.*, 1993) which is the period when children first begin to explore the wider envirionment without adult supervision, for example using public transport to and from school; this group of children in middle childhood needs particular attention.

● Research which focuses on the ethnic and cultural influences upon the ways in which responsibility for health is encouraged and shaped in the household context should be extended to cover other ethnic groups.

● Taking account of the increasing diversity of family forms is important. Children who live with and visit parents in different households negotiate health issues in the context of a further layer of complexity and need to be studied seriously with this in mind.

● Building on research methodologies which take children as subjects of research, studies should focus on children's views and constructions concerning health service provision and concerning appropriate communication and education with respect to health matters. Increasing importance is placed in policy and academic circles on taking into account children's right to be consulted concerning their care; an approach which focuses on children as active participants in services is required. These types of studies will help in the development of new interventions and health education curricula which in turn need to be evaluated against more traditional approaches.

1. Introduction

Personal responsibility is a key concept in health and health education. What is often forgotten is that responsibility is engendered in a social context. The particular social contexts and cultures which promote or discourage increased personal responsibility among children and young people with respect to health have, however, been too frequently ignored. In part this is because health education interventions have been mainly targeted at children and young people in one context, namely through schools. Children's health and health behaviour are shaped in a variety of contexts including home, school and other households containing kin, non-residential parents and friends, and in the neighbourhood and the wider society. With respect to household context, health education has taken little account of parents' employment patterns, household composition, cultural and ethnic backgrounds and the ways in which these interact with children's gender. All these factors shape children's and parents' attitudes and practices concerning the amount of personal responsibility and freedom children are given or negotiate for themselves.

Health education has also taken little account of the notion of change and transition with respect to the lives of children and their parents. Social transitions may be scheduled or unscheduled. They often constitute times of danger and opportunity for those undergoing them and therefore have consequences in terms of possibilities for action, especially health-related behaviour. Some of the most significant transitions relating to the structure of children's lives relate to stages in the educational system: starting school, the transfer to secondary school and so on. Transitions in parents' lives with possible health behavioural implications include the changes parents make in their employment – the move from part-time to full-time work or departure from the labour market altogether, and changes in household structure, such as becoming a single-parent household.

THE STUDY

This report is based on a study which locates the health and health-related behaviour of 11- to 12-year-olds in social context and in relation to the notion of social transition. The study focused on the effects of different kinds of parental employment contexts, mothers' employment in particular. It also examined children's health and health behaviour in relation to children's transfer from primary to secondary school. Both parental employment patterns and the transition to secondary school are likely to impinge on children's health behaviour since they affect the degree of responsibility and autonomy conferred on children. Parental employment patterns and the organisation of secondary schools also shape the resources provided for children's welfare and wellbeing and were therefore a key concern of the study. The study also focused on children's health behaviour in relation to the sex of parent and child, household composition and cultural background.

In the study, health was defined very broadly to include: perceptions of health and healthiness generally and specifically in relation to children themselves; children's food decisions at school; children's access to health education both at school and at home with respect to sex and puberty; children's smoking attitudes, behaviour and education; and their illness behaviour and accidents. These issues are discussed from both children's and parents' perspectives and the ways in which both parents and children negotiate different patterns of care and responsibility with respect to children's health.

The study was based on earlier research concerning health responsibility and household negotiations of 16-year-olds (Brannen *et al.*, 1994).

THE SOCIAL CONTEXT OF MOTHERS' EMPLOYMENT

There is a large amount of literature on the effects of parental employment and unemployment upon parents' own health and wellbeing while the effects upon other family members tend to be concentrated upon young children (for a literature review see Brannen *et al.*, 1994b). There is an international literature concerning the effects of mothers' employment upon children's health and development mediated by the influence of daycare and very little which relates to fathers' employment. The increasingly common situation in which both parents in a household are employed has important resource consequences in terms of income especially for older children and young people. In addition the situation in which mothers move into full-time employment is an important moment when children are likely to take greater responsibility for themselves and possibly for younger siblings. For example, research on teenagers (Brannen *et al.*, 1994) indicated that those young people whose mothers were employed full-time were likely to have greater responsibility for food preparation and for their own diet. In addition these young people were more likely to contribute to other household tasks compared with young people whose mothers worked part-time or not at all (Brannen, 1995). Parental employment is also likely to affect parents' practices concerning the care of children, for example what arrangements they make when children are ill (Hewison and Dowswell, 1994). These and other areas of 'health responsibility' were addressed in the current study. Mothers' employment rates have continued to rise in the United Kingdom and the pattern of dual (especially full-time) earner lifestyles has become more common. Mothers who leave employment to have children re-enter the labour market increasingly at more frequent intervals between births and earlier after births (Martin and Roberts, 1984). The rate at which they return to work rises as their children grow older; some mothers start work again while more increase their hours with significant movement from part-time to full-time employment. The *General Household Survey* reports economic activity rates for mothers by age of youngest child. With respect to part-time work, the rates reported in the 1992 *General Household Survey* (Thomas *et al.*, 1994) rise as dependent children get older: 31 per cent of those with a child aged 0–4 and 44 per cent of those with children aged 5–9 are employed. Of those with a child aged 10–16, 45 per cent are employed part-time. With respect to full-time work, the differences are more marked: of those with a child aged 0–4, 11 per cent are working; of those with children aged 5–9, 20 per cent are working while in the 10–16 group 31 per cent of mothers are employed full-time (as compared with 47 per cent of those with no dependent children).

The rates for lone mothers are, however, significantly lower than the employment rates for married mothers especially among some groups. With respect to part-time work, 14 per cent of lone mothers with a child under 5 are employed part-time while the figure rises to 32 per cent for those with a child aged 5–16, but is lower than the comparable figure of 47 per cent for married mothers. With respect to full-time work, only 8 per cent of lone mothers with a youngest child aged 0–4 are employed as are 26 per cent of those with a child aged 5–16, a similar proportion to married mothers (27 per cent). Unfortunately, no breakdown is given within the 5–16 age bracket for lone mothers.

Unemployment also declines as children get older, with unemployment lowest among women with a youngest child aged 16–18 (3 per cent), followed by those with a youngest child aged 10–15, 15 per cent for those with children aged 5–9, and highest among those with a child aged 0-4 (GHS data in Bridgwood and Savage, 1993). Parental non-employment patterns interact with household structures: lone-mother households are much more likely to have no parent in employment and, as noted, lone mothers are much less likely to engage in part-time work compared with mothers in two-parent households.

Increased responsibility at this point in children's lives may have different consequences in single- and two-parent households especially when parental employment patterns are also taken into account. Cultural origins of parents are also relevant since they may affect definitions of childhood and health responsibility. They too may be associated with particular patterns of household structure and parental employment. Finally, sex of child is also likely to be highly significant and, as in the earlier study, is likely to interact with other factors such as cultural origins.

THE TRANSITION FROM PRIMARY TO SECONDARY SCHOOL AND CHILDREN'S INCREASED RESPONSIBILITY

Just as health education needs to take account of the contexts of, and changes in, parents' lives so it should take account of the context and characteristics of children's lives. Transitions in children's lives are potential points for change in children's health beliefs and health behaviour. Moreover, children's transitions may signal changes in parents' lives. The potentially significant transition point of moving from primary to secondary school may affect mothers' employment with indirect consequences for children. The transition to secondary school may have direct effects on children: it may, for example, open children's horizons academically and widen their circle of peers. Both of these may confer on children new responsibilities and freedoms. For example, children may be allowed or encouraged to take themselves to and from school and to make food choices during the school day. Moreover, the transition from primary to secondary school is likely to be negotiated in different ways according to the sex of the child, his or her cultural origins and household type as well as being affected by parental employment.

As the previous study indicated, the way in which autonomy and responsibility are defined varies considerably. For example, there is a key distinction relating to responsibility for self as distinct from responsibility for others. In the earlier study of teenage health, young women were found to be significantly more likely than young men to bear certain kinds of health responsibility and household responsibility; in the latter case, this increased responsibility focused on the needs of others rather than on the needs of self (Brannen, 1995). The earlier study also indicated that different cultural groups attached very different values to growing up. UK-born parents expect their young people to have greater individual autonomy at 16, compared with Asian-origin parents, and are more likely to negotiate young people's increased individual independence through communication. Asian-origin families confer greater responsibility on young people according to the norms of age grading but do not view adolescence as necessarily involving individual rights to independence of, and separation from, their families. Moreover, their strategies of control are more transparent since they expect young people to abide by culturally specified norms which are therefore less subject to negotiation via communication than those applying in UK-origin families. Gender and culture also interact with one another with the result that Asian young women are expected to have considerable responsibility in the household though not necessarily to have much individual autonomy with respect to activities outside the home and for making decisions about their personal health. Their parents are more also restrictive of young women than young men.

A CHILD-CENTRED APPROACH TO HEALTH

Issues of children's care, responsibility and autonomy were addressed in this study from a broad health perspective. Health is part and parcel of the fabric of routine everyday family life as it is lived by children and as it is played out by mothers and fathers in their parenting of children. The study therefore focused on the health perspectives of children themselves – their health and healthiness, their body image and fitness together with children's activities including the more obviously health-related topics such as diet and food practices and participation in sports. Home-based activities such as 'playing' with their computers, watching television and contributing to household tasks were also investigated together with going 'out and about' in the street and the wider world between home and school. These too have significant health consequences.

In this study we adopted a similar perspective to our previous study and construed children as active agents in the conduct of their own lives. This involved treating children as competent research participants, and as the subjects rather than the objects of research. As Solberg (1996) has suggested, in this endeavour we did not seek to take their age into account. Rather we were concerned to elicit children's views and to take their accounts seriously in the way that we approach all respondents. Moreover, we found children to be reliable and competent informants on their parents' situations, for example their employment and occupations.

THE IMPORTANCE OF THE STUDY IN POLICY TERMS

The focus of the study on the contexts and situations in which children acquire increased personal responsibility is justified in policy terms on the grounds that health education curricula need to be made more relevant to the experiences and social circumstances of children and their families if they are to have the desired effect. In particular, health education programmes and materials may usefully be developed to adopt a life-course perspective which covers the social transitions which children and parents experience. They should also take a macroperspective which takes account of social structural change in society both in terms of changing family forms and household composition and in the labour market, especially the growing polarised pattern of work-rich and work-poor households (Gregg and Wadsworth, 1995). In adopting this health education approach it is necessary to take the child's perspective as well as that of adults by attending to the ways in which children themselves view health, health responsibility and health education in the contexts of their own lives.

Positioning the children as the subjects of research has implications for the positioning of children as recipients of health education and the ways in which they reconstruct the information for themselves. Moreover, the theoretical and methodological aspects of the study constitute groundwork for policy development in terms of generating a variety of health education approaches targeted at particular groups, and suggest the need to evaluate health education programmes in the light of different types of approaches. Child-led or child-informed health education which takes account of the changing contexts of children's lives – home, school, peer groups and in the community – is an important tool for the future.

2. The study's design and methods

The present study in its design and methods replicates an earlier study of 16-year-olds and their negotiation of health responsibility with parents (Brannen *et al.*, 1994). The study focuses on a younger age group, namely 11- to 12-year-olds. It involved a two-stage design: a self-completion questionnaire survey carried out in schools and a series of case studies of households including interviews with children and their parents conducted in the home.

THE QUESTIONNAIRE SURVEY

The questionnaire survey was conducted with first years (year 7) in three secondary schools in a west London borough. We used the questionnaire from the previous study as a model but with some considerable adaptation for a younger age group. In the earlier study we included some questions from Balding's Health-related Behaviour Questionnaire (Balding, 1993). In this study we also drew upon the HEA's *Tomorrow's Young Adults* (HEA, 1992) and the *General Household Survey 1990* (Smyth and Browne, 1992) in designing some of the questions. The questionnaire consisted of a hundred questions which ranged over a wide field: for example, the transition to secondary school, rules and responsibilities at home, health and health-related behaviours and leisure activities. As employment was a key focus of the study and in order to ensure a high response rate we included questions on parents' employment in an early part of the questionnaire. We also asked those whose mothers worked if their mothers had changed their working hours or pattern since they, the children, had started secondary school.

We approached the same west London state schools used in the original study (Brannen *et al.*, 1994). In the event, having discussed the survey's objectives and the research strategy with the schools' headteachers, we were able to survey only three of the four schools, yielding a total of 536 respondents. Letters from the school heads requesting parental consent were dispatched via the children before the questionnaire survey was administered and, as a consequence, two pupils were excluded from the survey because of parental refusal. We piloted a questionnaire during the first week of March 1994 on one class in one of the selected schools. With minor modification the questionnaires were administered during the fortnight beginning 14 March 1994, utilising personal and social education curriculum time. School staff were, in the main, enthusiastic about the project, although they were generally pessimistic about the reading ability of their new intake. Curriculum pressures also exercised constraint on the time that staff were able to allocate to the project. However, pupils, even those with reading and comprehension difficulties, appeared highly motivated in answering the questions and those who had not completed the questionnaire in the allotted time stayed behind during the lunch or morning breaks. Absenteeism was not a problem with this age group. The overall response rate for the three schools was 92 per cent of pupils (95 per cent, 90 per cent and 92 per cent in each school). This compares with an overall response rate in the previous study of 15- to 16-year-olds of 85 per cent.

The questionnaire responses were analysed using SPSS (Statistical Package in the

Social Sciences) and to recompense each school for its help, we provided each with a report and detailed quantitative data analyses with respect to their particular school.

The sample contained 249 girls and 287 boys. Based on two questions on ethnicity concerning parents' countries of origin and the children's views of their ethnic affiliation, four broad ethnic categories were created. Fifty-eight per cent were classified as white, mainly UK-origin but also including 4 per cent identified as coming from other Western and eastern European countries. Although 21 per cent of the sample were of Asian-origin, many were from families who came to the UK from East Africa and the Middle East; within this Asian group, over half identified their parents to be of Indian-origin, around 15 per cent were from Pakistan and three per cent came from Bangladesh. Overall 16 per cent of the sample were classified as black, 8 per cent of Caribbean-origin and 8 per cent of African origin. Five per cent were placed in a miscellaneous 'Other' group, principally children of Middle Eastern origin or from South East Asia. Ethnic composition varies by school with Asian origin children comprising 39 per cent in School 1, 17 per cent in School 2 and 7 per cent in School 3; white or UK origin is 36 per cent in School 1, 70 per cent in School 2 and 68 per cent in School 3; black pupils comprised 19 per cent of School 1, 10 per cent of School 2 and 20 per cent of School 3.

Children were asked to circle those persons present in their households and to write in the names of additional people who were not on the list indicated on the questionnaire. Overall, 72 per cent of the sample reported living with their biological mother and father and 8 per cent with mother and stepfather or mother's cohabitee. Sixteen per cent lived with their lone mother and the remaining 4 per cent were in other household arrangements (5 children with lone fathers, 3 with father and stepmother or father's girlfriend and 5 with foster parents or other guardians). When household composition and ethnic origin are considered together, almost 90 per cent of Asian-origin children reported living with both birth parents compared with only 74 per cent of the white children and 47 per cent of the black children. A mother and stepfather arrangement was virtually non-existent in the Asian-origin group. Lone-mother households were highest in the black group with 35 per cent of the children reporting this arrangement compared with 14 per cent of those of white and 10 per cent of the Asian-origin group.

HOUSEHOLD CASE STUDIES

The schools' questionnaire survey provided us with the basis for the second phase of the study. This phase consisted of a series of 31 case studies of families involving interviews with children and their mothers and fathers. The sample was differentiated by three variables: (a) sex of the children; (b) cultural group (Asian-origin parents constitute one of the largest ethnic groups in the study area and questionnaire sample and we therefore selected these families in addition to a similar-sized group of UK-origin households); and (c) household composition (two-parent families versus single-mother families). Intensive in-depth interviews using a semi-structured schedule were carried out separately with each child and parent and tape-recorded for transcription to disk. The material was coded to allow for both quantitative and qualitative data analysis.

Drawing on the questionnaire survey data, the sampling strategy aimed to produce 16 categories of households with two households in each. The schools sent letters to all the pupils in year 7 asking their parents to reply only if they did not wish to take part in the project. We contacted parents by letter in late June 1994 and largely completed interviewing by the end of the summer holidays. In total, 54 households were approached and household members from 31 of these were interviewed. Of the other 22 households, not all were refusals since in some cases the category into which they fell was full or because further questioning revealed that they were no longer suitable for inclusion according to the selected criteria.

Nine households gave outright refusals or were not available. In one case, the parents were initially happy to be interviewed but the child was not, so the parents declined. In another case the mother was going into hospital; in a further case the family was just about to move house and another selected household had already moved away from the area.

We set targets for the household study of 16 two-parent households and 16 lone-mother households. Within each of these two types of households we aimed to interview eight mothers working full-time and eight non-employed, and again split equally between Asian-origin and UK-origin households. Target interviews were more difficult to achieve in some categories than others. We had no difficulty in finding two-parent households, since the questionnaire survey provided us with plenty of examples. In total, we interviewed 18 households with two birth parents in residence, two in each of the eight categories plus one UK-origin white family and one Asian-origin family in which the mother worked technically part-time. From these 18 households we achieved interviews with 13 fathers and 13 mothers. Of the 'missing' fathers, one was of UK origin and four of Asian origin. Two of the Asian-origin fathers were reported to be too busy; one worked away from home all week. The one UK-origin father refused outright without explanation. The four mothers were all of Asian origin; two posed language problems, one refused along with the father, and the husband of the fourth refused on behalf of his wife although he was interviewed. In all, the maximum of three interviews were achieved in 10 of the 18 two-parent households.

The lone-mother households proved more problematic, since we had fewer households from which to choose for each of our target categories. Indeed, we found only two Asian-origin lone mothers who worked full-time in the whole questionnaire survey. Of the lone Asian-origin mothers we did interview, one had two part-time jobs and the other one had in fact given up work. We were able to interview only three UK-origin, non-employed single mothers. Overall, we interviewed 13 single-mother households, having missed our target by three. The Asian-origin single mothers were mainly widowed with only two out of the six being divorced, whilst the UK-origin lone mothers presented contrasting life histories, with six divorced or separated from the fathers of the children and one who had never married.

In total, 13 fathers, 26 mothers and 16 boys and 18 girls were interviewed, in 31 households. This included three pairs of same-sex twins.

3. Parents' employment and children's care after school

This chapter presents evidence of parental employment patterns in the context of children's move to secondary school. It examines how far mothers' employment affects children's care after school. It presents material concerning children's reports of parental rules concerning being at home alone and being out of the house alone together with children's own attitudes on these issues. Mothers' attitudes to their presence or absence are also considered, as are children's feelings of responsibility since the transition to secondary school.

MOTHERS' EMPLOYMENT WHEN CHILDREN START SECONDARY SCHOOL

Over 66 per cent of children report that their (resident) mothers are in paid work, with 16 per cent housewives, 6 per cent unemployed, and 2 per cent students. Nine per cent of children reported their mother not working, but did not indicate which non-working category they were in. The division between part- and full-time employment status is as follows: 33 per cent in full-time work, 33 per cent in part-time or paid work at home. Ethnic background makes little difference to the rate of employment amongst mothers. However, whereas 30 per cent of both white and Asian-origin mothers are working full-time, a much higher proportion of black mothers (42 per cent) work full-time.

With respect to household composition in relation to the employment status of the mothers, 51 per cent of the lone mothers are employed compared with 69 per cent of the mothers in two-parent households (Table 3.1). For mothers in two-parent households, 33 per cent work full-time compared with 32 per cent of the single mothers. However, only 19 per cent of lone mothers are in part-time employment compared with 36 per cent of mothers in two-parent households.

Table 3.2 indicates that children's birth order is the strongest determinant of mothers' employment. When living arrangement is also taken into account, where the child is the youngest in the household and the mother is part of a couple, 41 per cent report their mother working full-time compared with only 27 per cent of those who have younger siblings at home. Part-time work does not discriminate. A similar difference is found among lone mothers with respect to full-time work, taking account of birth order. Where the mother is on her own and the child is the youngest in the household, 45 per cent report their mother working full-time compared with 21 per cent who have younger siblings.

On the basis of the case study evidence, the study provides only limited evidence of mothers moving into employment or increasing their hours *during* their child's *first year* at secondary school. However, it does suggest that many are contemplating change around this time although decisions clearly relate to a diverse range of family commitments not only those concerning the target children. The factors which promote or inhibit employment change are clearly complex and were not the focus of the study.

Table 3.1 Mothers'* employment status and household composition by ethnicity (numbers and percentages): questionnaire survey

	Full-time		Part-time		Not working		No info	Total
	n	%	n	%	n	%	n	N
Two-parent households								
All	142	33	156	36	128	30	5	433
Asian	32	32	34	34	33	33	1	100
White	81	31	105	40	72	28	3	261
Black	20	41	14	29	14	29	1	49
Other	9	[9]	3	[3]	9	[9]	0	[21]
Lone mothers								
All	28	32	17	19	39	49	3	88
Asian	2	[2]	2	[2]	7	[7]	0	11
White	12	29	9	21	20	48	1	42
Black	13	43	6	20	10	33	1	30
Other	1	[1]	0	0	2	[2]	1	4

* Birth mothers only
[ ] indicates number not percentage

Table 3.2 Mothers'* employment status by household composition by presence of younger children (numbers and percentages): questionnaire survey

	Full-time		Part-time		Not working		Total
	n	%	n	%	n	%	N
Respondent has no younger siblings							
Two-parent	75	41	63	35	42	24	180
Lone mothers	18	45	6	15	16	40	40
Respondent has younger siblings†							
Two-parent	67	27	94	37	92	36	253
Lone mothers	10	21	11	23	27	56	48

* Birth mothers only
† Only-children are included with those reporting no younger siblings

FATHERS' AND HOUSEHOLD EMPLOYMENT

Eighty-four per cent of resident fathers are reported by children to be in employment and 15 per cent (61) not at work for a variety of reasons including unemployment, retirement and sickness. Only four respondents (1 per cent) with resident fathers failed to answer the question. A further seven, whilst reporting that their fathers worked, failed to identify whether this was full-time or part-time. Ninety per cent of white resident fathers are in paid work, with 76 per cent reported as working full-time; 79 per cent of Asian-origin resident fathers are in employment with 58 per cent full-time; and 65 per cent of black resident fathers are employed with 51 per cent in full-time work.

Over half the two-parent households have two wage-earners while 19 per cent have only one parent in part-time employment or no parent working. In contrast just under half the one-parent households have no one working, with 32 per cent having their parent in full-time employment. No significant differences are found by ethnicity in terms of having two parents in full-time employment. However, ethnic differences are found with respect to the more typical household employment pattern – father full-time and mother in part-time work: 34 per cent of the white two-parent families compared with 22 per cent of Asian-origin families and 24 per cent (12/50) of black families. Again, the presence or absence of younger siblings is significant with respect to household employment patterns. Thirty-two per cent of youngest children living in two-parent households report both parents working full-time compared with 21 per cent of eldest respondents and 20 per cent of 'middle' children, i.e. those with both older and younger siblings present in the household. (An even higher incidence is reported by only-children with 9/27 having both parents working full-time.)

PARENTAL EMPLOYMENT AND CHILDREN'S CARE AFTER SCHOOL

Despite the high proportion of mothers in employment, few 11- to 12-year-olds were cared for after school outside the home on a formal basis. Two-thirds of children in the questionnaire survey report that someone was usually at home after school; only 5 per cent say there is never anyone else there. Girls are significantly more likely to report someone there.

Moreover, the extent to which mothers organised their working hours and working patterns around their children was striking. Most often the mother is at home or both parents (in 77 per cent of cases), with youngest children least likely to report presence of mother and most likely to report presence of other siblings. Over a quarter say that they are on their own more compared with when they were at middle school and just over a fifth said they are alone less. Asian-origin children are unlikely to be on their own at home, i.e. without adults; some have resident grandmothers who look after them. In contrast white children and black children were more likely to say they are on their own at home more since starting secondary school compared with Asian-origin children.

Those whose mothers are employed full-time are more likely to report being on their own more since starting secondary school compared with those whose mothers work part-time or not at all. Those most likely to report no one at home are children of lone, full-time employed mothers (part-time work is rare among lone mothers) followed by children with two full-time employed parents. Similar patterns are reported with respect to spending time alone at half term.

Children's activities in the house after school are influenced to some extent by parental employment status with children of employed parents reporting doing homework and reading a book more frequently while those whose mothers are not employed are more likely to play with computer games and to watch videos more frequently.

Over a quarter of children report that they are doing more in the way of household chores since starting secondary school while just under a fifth are doing less. Those whose mothers are working full-time are more likely to report doing more compared with those whose mothers are part-time or not employed.

INSIDE AND OUTSIDE HOME: PARENTAL RULES AND CHILDREN'S VIEWS

Most parents are said by their children to have some rules about being at home alone, with girls more likely to report parental rules. However no differences are found with respect to the employment status of either mothers or fathers nor with respect to household composition, birth order or ethnic origin of the children. Over half of children, particularly boys, think it is okay to be in the house alone but a significant proportion is unsure. Presence of siblings and household type makes no difference here. However, ethnicity is significant, with Asian origin boys and girls more likely to think it not okay compared with white children. Similarly, children whose mothers are not employed are rather more sceptical while those whose parents are both in full-time work are most in favour of being alone in the house.

Children and parents in the case studies report considerable restrictions about what children should and should not do in their parents' absence, for example what to do if a stranger knocks on the door, with girls subject to rather more restriction than boys, and two-parent families and parents of older children reported to be rather more rule-inclined.

In general children express equanimity about being at home alone rather than enthusiasm or discomfort. Girls in general and children of Asian origin are less happy, expressing worry or fear, together with those whose mothers did not work or who worked part-time. Those who liked being at home alone (typically boys in general, white children and those with full-time employed mothers) mention the feeling of being trusted and the opportunity to pursue their own interests.

Children were also asked about being out of the house on their own; nearly half say parents have 'flexible' rules with the rest more or less equally split between those who say their parents have no rules and those who operate strict rules. Asian-origin boys and girls are significantly more likely than their white peers to say their parents are strict about being out of the house on their own. With respect to being out after dark, over two-thirds say their parents are strict on this issue, a quarter flexible and only 7 per cent are said to have no rules. Parents of boys and those of Asian origin are most likely to be reported strict and sons of Asian origin-parents are significantly more likely to say so compared with sons of white parents. A similar trend is found with respect to girls but differences are not significant, reflecting the high proportion of girls in all groups reporting strict parents.

Children were asked the specific question relating to this issue: whether they think it okay or not to travel to and from school alone. Most say they think it okay (86 per cent) but those of Asian origin are significantly less likely to say so. In the case studies children were asked about travel to school and four-fifths say their schools are further away than their primary schools. Over half have increased responsibility for taking themselves to and from school involving negotiating public transport or longer walks to school. About a third walk to or from school, a third go by bus, about a fifth by car (with fewer travelling home by car), and the rest mainly by train. These figures suggest that this metropolitan group walk less than the average child as described in national data (Church and Summerfield, 1994). Travel type is related to household employment patterns with children of single mothers who are not in employment least likely to travel by car. In two-parent households, those with one or more parent in employment tend to use the train compared with those whose parents are not in work. Sex differences are also apparent (more girls than boys travelling by car) but are not significant. Asian-origin children are significantly more likely to travel by car, typically with fathers on their way to work, and are less likely to go by public transport.

MOTHERS' CONCERNS ABOUT CHILDREN'S CARE

In contrast to their children, mothers are highly concerned about their own presence or absence when children get in from school. If they are present, UK-origin mothers emphasise the psychological advantages for children, especially the way mothers 'being there' gives children a sense of security. By contrast, Asian-origin mothers stress the importance of their physical protection of their children from the dangers of the external world.

Where UK-origin mothers leave their children on their own (usually only for short periods), they attribute benefits to this practice and make reference to the developmental paradigm, namely the ways in which children need to learn to become more independent. Even those who do not leave their children alone at home talk in these terms and make judgements about whether their children are 'quite ready' for the desired first steps into independence. At the same time these mothers were fearful of being judged neglectful mothers by leaving them 'too early'. Asian-origin mothers do not suggest that their absence increases and thereby benefits their children's independence.

CHILDREN'S SENSE OF RESPONSIBILITY SINCE STARTING SECONDARY SCHOOL

Over three-quarters of children feel they are more responsible since starting secondary school; no significant differences are found with respect to sex of child, ethnicity or birth order and only slight (but not significant differences) according to mothers' employment with respect to an increased sense of responsibility among children of full-time employed mothers.

In discussing their sense of responsibility, none of the children spontaneously refers to their parents' employment or to being on their own more. Rather the reasons they give for an increased sense of responsibility appear to lie in the changed conditions of children's lives related to starting secondary school and their lives in school including the associated change in attitudes on the part of teachers, parents and others. For example, many children experience a longer and generally unescorted journey to school, the need for more planning and organisation because of the demands of a higher level of school, and an increased sense of responsibility for self engendered by the move itself – 'now you're at secondary school'. Indeed, when asked in the questionnaire about the problems of starting secondary school, a number of children mentioned the increase in self-responsibility: 'organising myself' and 'getting up at 7.00 a.m. and packing my bag'. However, it is interesting to note that there is no difference between those who travel alone to school and those who go with others in their response to the responsibility question.

SUMMARY POINTS

The study provides evidence to suggest high maternal employment rates (66 per cent) among children starting secondary school. The questionnaire survey evidence based on children's reports indicates that children are able and reliable informants of parental employment status and occupation; reliability was checked in those cases where parents were subsequently interviewed in the second part of the study. It suggests mothers are significantly more likely to be employed *by the time* their youngest or only child starts secondary school especially in full-time employment (33 per cent). The study provides only limited evidence of mothers *moving into* employment or increasing their hours during their child's first year at secondary school. However, the qualitative case study data suggest that many mothers are contemplating change around this time although decisions clearly relate to a diverse range of family commitments, not only those related to the target children. The factors which promote or inhibit employment change are clearly complex and were not the focus of the study.

Whether mothers are living with their children's fathers is also important and determines whether mothers are in the labour market at all, with high rates of non-employment among lone mothers. However, rates of full-time employment do not differ between married/cohabiting and lone mothers. Ethnicity also affects mothers' employment patterns. Black mothers are more likely to be working full-time, whatever their household composition, while white mothers are most likely to work part-time (in two-parent households) and Asian-origin mothers to be non-employed.

For some children, starting secondary school means greater independence in terms of being at home by themselves after school until parents arrive home from work. Those whose mothers work full-time, especially those whose lone mothers are employed full-time, are more likely to report being on their own more at home since starting secondary school. However, only under a quarter report neither parent normally being at home when children get in from school. Over half have increased responsibility for taking themselves to and from school, with only a third walking and a fifth going by car with the rest using public transport.

Most parents are reported to have rules for children about what they should and should not do when they are at home without adults but children of employed parents were no more or less likely to report rules. Over half the children themselves think being at home alone is all right but a significant proportion is unsure, with girls and Asian-origin children more likely to think it not okay compared with boys and white children. Those whose mothers are not employed are more sceptical about the advisability of being at home alone compared with those with mothers in employment. A pattern of parental restriction is found with respect to rules about being out of the house, especially after dark.

Mothers express concern about being present when their children get in from school. However, UK-origin mothers are more likely to claim benefits for their children in terms of the opportunity for developing a sense of independence if their children spend any time at home alone. Mothers evaluate how far their children are 'ready', i.e. psychologically and emotionally mature, to take what they see to be significant first steps into independence. Asian-origin mothers do not refer to this developmental framework.

Most children describe themselves as feeling more responsible since starting secondary school, with no significant differences according to any of the main factors covered by the study. Children attribute these feelings to the new pattern of their lives at secondary school and to parents' and teachers' expectations of them.

4. Perceptions of children's health and healthiness

This chapter looks at children's assessments of their own health and the criteria they use in constructing their assessments, then at their parents' views of their children's health and the meanings that they attach to the notion of health. For most children and parents, these assessments focus on diet and fitness which in turn manifest themselves in concerns about physical appearance. The chapter also explores how children feel about their bodies, whether they are satisfied with their physical selves and, if not, the strategies they adopt in order to make changes.

CHILDREN'S HEALTH ASSESSMENTS AND LIFESTYLE LINKS

In the questionnaire survey, few children perceive their health in definitively positive terms. Thirty-four per cent say that it is 'good' while 48 per cent report it as 'fairly good'. However, only 9 per cent feel their health is 'not good'. A further 9 per cent are unsure. These assessments of health status are not differentiated by their mothers' or fathers' employment nor by occupational status, ethnic origin or the sex of the child.

Children frequently link their health status to eating healthy or unhealthy food or to eating in excess. A UK-origin girl says 'I can't just say my health is really good because I know it's not, because of the eating wise' (sic). An Asian-origin girl sees herself as 'not so good' in health terms: 'I eat too much and I am getting lazier', making implicit reference to lack of fitness.

Two boys who talk about their diet in this context both assess their health as 'quite good', with an Asian-origin boy qualifying his answer: 'Because I eat chocolates. I think I shouldn't eat them but I can't help it'. By contrast, a UK-origin boy presents his diet as making a positive and a negative contribution to his healthiness: 'Cos I eat healthy things and fat things as well'.

Two children, both boys, define their health solely in terms of physical fitness. 'Good – because I am fit' said a UK-born boy, and an Asian-origin boy said: 'I reckon it's quite good cos we had a fitness test in school and I came second out of my class'.

These self-evaluations linked to lifestyle demonstrate the ways in which the children perceive the state of their health as contingent upon themselves, what they do and therefore within their own locus of control. They see their health in part as their own personal responsibility: 'because I am fit', 'because I eat healthy things', 'because I eat too much'. Moreover, children recognise that they are making a contribution, either positively or negatively, to the state of their *bodily* health. No mention is made of health as a mental state or in terms of generalised wellbeing. These definitions of health suggest that children have well understood the messages of health educators who define health primarily in terms of personal lifestyles.

PARENTS' ASSESSMENTS OF THEIR CHILDREN'S HEALTH

In the case studies, parents of 23 children rate their children's health as good, only 6 as quite good and 3 as not good. In households where both parents were interviewed, fathers and mothers are in agreement in eight cases. In four cases where parents disagree, the child's health is rated as quite good by the father and good by the mother in three cases; in the other case, the positions are reversed.

Research has suggested that mothers whose children have poor health are less likely to engage in paid work compared with those whose children are more healthy (Hewison and Dowswell, 1994). Rather more of the employed mothers (12/15) report their children's health as good compared with 7 of the 11 non-working mothers. However, the two mothers who report their children's health as not so good work full-time.

Parents, like their children, use the criteria of lifestyle – notably diet and physical fitness – in assessing their children's healthiness. Additionally some parents stress illness or the absence of illness. Eleven of the 26 mothers qualified or justified their assessments in terms of illness histories; three rate their child's health as not good because of current illness; five as healthy, despite citing current illness; and three as healthy because of an absence of illness. Five of the 13 fathers mention their children's health in terms of illness, one in terms of his son's fitness and weight, another in terms of his daughter being overweight.

Compared with the children, parents are generally more optimistic about their children's health. Sixteen children rate their health as quite good whilst the parent is more positive and rates it as good. In ten cases parents agree with children in their evaluations of the children's health, and in five cases the parents think the children's health is not as good as the children describe.

CHILDREN'S VIEWS ON HEALTHY LIFESTYLES: FOOD AND FITNESS

Fourteen children in the case studies say that they have healthy lifestyles, while 13 think their lifestyle is mixed, with healthy and unhealthy aspects to it. Four girls and two boys feel that their way of life is unhealthy. Again, children present evidence from their eating and exercise habits to describe their lifestyles. Exceptionally, one boy expresses his healthiness in terms of good personal hygiene and two UK-origin girls see their healthiness as not indulging in the risky behaviours associated with teenagers:

> 'Cos I don't smoke and drink and that, take drugs and that I lead a sort of healthy life.

> Because I don't smoke or I don't do drugs. I eat the right food sometimes.

Asked about what they do that is healthy and unhealthy, many answers refer to the 'right' and 'wrong' foods. Seven girls and five boys emphasised the healthiness of their diets, but four girls and three boys speak negatively about what they eat. A healthy diet is seen to involve *not* eating unhealthy foods as well as eating healthy foods, avoiding eating too much, avoiding sweets and chocolate, 'fatty' or 'junk' food, and foods cooked in unhealthy ways.

Three girls and four boys present a mixed picture. They cite healthy foods they eat regularly but stress too the unhealthiness of other aspects, suggesting that eating the former will assuage the negative effects of the latter.

Children's perceptions of their lifestyles include references to fitness and physical activity. Sixteen children judge themselves in terms of their fitness or sporting activity and four mention their healthiness solely in those terms. Five girls and one boy talk about their need to take more exercise. However, girls are particularly likely to make adverse comments about PE or school sports. In particular they single out the aggressive ethos of sport at school and the unseemliness of the PE kit. By contrast, girls see aerobics and cycling as more acceptable forms of exercise, neither of which is normally part of schools sports curricula. PE tends to alienate the girls rather than provide a positive health education message:

> I go to the netball club but I just don't get along with the teachers in sports. . . . they're very aggressive most of them. We have to do press-ups if we are late or something and they are quite harsh. We have to go out in the rain and snow and sleet in hockey.

Boys were more enthusiastic about PE and sports at school. Five of the boys belong to sports clubs, both inside and outside school. None of the girls mentions belonging to such clubs. One Asian-origin girl says that she would like to join after-school tennis and athletic clubs but the long walk home afterwards deters her. Also her mother insists that she comes straight home from school.

PHYSICAL ACTIVITY: PARENTAL EMPLOYMENT, SEX AND ETHNICITY

In the questionnaire survey, no differences are found by mothers' employment concerning children's use of sports or leisure centres. Similarly, with household employment patterns, there is no reported difference in the use of sports or leisure facilities. However, boys report higher levels of physical activity than girls: 29 per cent of boys but only 7 per cent of girls say that they have undertaken a physical sport outside school every day. There are significant differences also in the frequency of going to sports centres; 48 per cent of boys and 30 per cent of girls report going to a sports centre in the past week. There are differences too by ethnicity, with Asian-origin girls least likely to have been to a sports or leisure centre in the preceding week: only 21 per cent have visited a sports centre in the past week compared with 33 per cent of white girls, 50 per cent of white boys and 56 per cent of Asian boys (Table 4.1).

In the interview case studies, four girls and seven boys have been to a sports centre in the previous week, and four girls and nine boys have taken part in a physical sport or activity outside school. Significantly, the four Asian boys who visited sports centres have all been with members of their families, three with mothers and one

Table 4.1   Children visiting sports or leisure centres and playing a physical sport outside school in past week by sex and ethnicity: questionnaire survey

	Visited sports centre		Played a sport		Total	
	girls %	boys %	girls %	boys %	girls N	boys N
All	30	48	50	76	224	267
Asian	21	56	39	76	54	45
White	33	50	53	76	134	154
Black	30	38	58	72	26	50
Other	25	41	62	94	8	16

with his father. None of the Asian girls has been at all, and of the four white girls, two have been with friends and two with their families. For Asian-origin girls, sport and games outside school appear strictly home-based, either indoors or in the back garden.

PARENTS' VIEWS OF CHILDREN'S LIFESTYLES

Like the children, parents discuss their children's lifestyle in terms of nutrition and, to a lesser extent, physical exercise. Fifteen mothers talk of healthiness of lifestyle in terms of diet whilst eight mention exercise; six speak in terms of both. Five define healthy lifestyles in the wider perspective of healthy minds and the general socialisation of their children:

> Healthy mind in their activities and what they do and their attitude towards their school and their work. (UK-origin mother in two-parent household)

> Healthy eating, healthy thinking as well. Going out and socialising is very important. (Asian-origin lone mother)

> He gets plenty of exercise, I try to give him the right foods. He has got quite a good range of interests, he is good company, he is not narrow-minded, he enjoys the fresh air, he enjoys swimming. (UK-origin lone mother)

CHILDREN'S SATISFACTION WITH THEIR BODY IMAGE

By the age of 11 or 12, there is a considerable range in children's physical development. Some have already experienced an adolescent growth spurt whilst others are in the pre-pubescent phase. Clearly these changes may be anxiety-provoking for children. Many children interpret the changes taking place in their bodies as counter to the dictates of fashion which define slimness as desirable. In a study of 15-year-olds in Australia, Kirk and Tinning (1994) report that the process of constructing embodied self-identity is focused on notions of normality, of feeling accepted and of avoiding exposure or embarrassment.

Many children, notably girls, undergoing puberty perceive themselves to be overweight and are alarmed at the unexpected weight increase at this point in their development. Just over half of children (58 per cent) in the questionnaire survey say that they are happy with their bodies. Girls are significantly less happy than boys: 50 per cent say they are happy compared with 65 per cent of boys (Table 4.2). More girls than boys (32 per cent versus 20 per cent) have mixed feelings and report themselves as both happy and unhappy with their shape.

Table 4.2 Children's satisfaction with their shape, weight and height: questionnaire survey

	Girls %	Boys %
Very happy or happy	50	65
Happy and unhappy	32	20
Unhappy or very unhappy	16	11
Not sure	2	4
N	248	287

Boys also report significantly more satisfaction than girls with their weight; many more girls say that they would like to lose weight. Forty-one per cent of boys and 29 per cent of girls are happy with their weight. Nearly half the girls say that they would like to lose weight. This compares with less than a quarter of the boys, but 15 per cent of the boys and 11 per cent of girls wish to put on weight. Boys are more likely than girls not to think about their weight: 21 per cent of boys and 12 per cent of girls claim never to think about their weight. There are no significant differences by mothers' employment status or occupational status of mothers or fathers.

Table 4.3   Children's preferences concerning weight by sex: questionnaire survey

	Girls %	Boys %
Would like to put on weight	11	15
Would like to lose weight	48	23
Happy with my present weight	29	41
Never think about my weight	12	21
N	248	284

CHILDREN'S PERCEPTIONS OF THEIR BODY IMAGE

In the questionnaire survey, 25 per cent of girls (62) responded to an open-ended question that they thought themselves overweight or fat. Only 9 per cent of boys say this. Girls are particularly concerned about their legs and their stomachs. Seven per cent of boys and 6 per cent of girls think themselves too thin or underweight. A small proportion of boys (4 per cent) say that they are too short. However, in the interviews, half the girls and a quarter of the boys say that they are fat or would like to be slimmer. Two Asian boys see themselves as too thin and would like to put on weight.

Dissatisfaction with appearance was explored in some detail in the case studies. Motivations to achieve the idealised norm of slim appearance are, for girls, related to their perceptions of their peers, seeing their friends to be slimmer than themselves. In two cases, adverse criticism and bullying from other pupils is cited:

> Well, they would call me a fat bitch and things like that, but now I don't get called a thing. Obviously I get called it for fun, from my friends but not constantly.

> I used to be so skinny and when I look through my photo album ... I have got photos of me when I was really skinny and dressed up and it really makes me sick to see that I have put on so much weight.

Some children claim that they want to be slimmer for themselves, not because they care about what other people think. 'I'll be more happy with myself' was a frequently cited motivation for being slimmer.

Parents report reassuring their children with comments about weight problems 'running in the family', and fatness being a natural phase of adolescence. In only one case were such reassurances repeated by the child to the interviewer. A boy quotes his mother as telling him that, as he grows, he will 'thin out'. Clearly despite parents trying to normalise children's weight through reference to either genetic or developmental stage, children themselves are heavily influenced by the dictates of the idealised norm of slimness.

CHILDREN'S STRATEGIES FOR ACHIEVING IDEAL BODY IMAGE

The strategies girls adopt to achieve the ideal shape range through doing very little, to taking exercise and to serious attempts at dieting. Getting fit, taking exercise with dancing or aerobics classes are mentioned as the 'right way' to achieve slimness. A girl who has been bullied because of her weight is adamant that she will not go on a diet because 'diets are stupid – if you start a diet you will be dieting for the rest of your life.' Others report that they have tried to diet with varying degrees of success: it 'didn't work' or it was 'difficult to keep to' were common responses. This girl, teased at school for being overweight, perceives the problem as her own responsibility. She sees her parents as helping to control her eating at home but ultimately it is up to her to make the effort to resist temptations:

> . . . in my house I normally eat healthily. But when I go out I buy rubbish which can't be stopped. Because my mum and dad aren't here to stop me so I can't rely on them all the time anyway . . . It's usually when I go out with my friends. There are shops just around the corner from there. They always have money and go round the corner, so I try and get money and go round the corner.

This sense of self-responsibility is evident with at least a quarter of the potential slimmers setting themselves goals or making themselves promises about slimming. Children say dieting is particularly difficult at school or when they are out with friends. Since interviewing took place during and around the school summer holidays, the holidays featured not surprisingly in the children's comments. Some say they find the holidays an easier time to slim, suggesting that the school environment may be a hostile one in which to develop a strategy to control eating; temptations are too readily available and peer pressure to indulge in snacks and chips is too great.

PARENTS' VIEWS OF THEIR CHILDREN'S BODY IMAGE

Most parents feel that their children's fears about being fat or overweight are unfounded at this age. Children's weight gain is explained as part of the natural course of the biological development of early adolescence or as a consequence of genetic tendencies. Parents say that they stress to their children the importance of eating healthily, that the child will slim down as he or she gets older, and that exercise will solve any problems. Generally they are against serious dieting and only three acknowledge that their children have real problems with weight. Others perceive no problems and dismiss their children's weight concerns. One UK-origin mother blames the media and fashion for promoting worries about ideal body shape.

Only three mothers acknowledge that limiting the intake of food may be a solution to their child's weight problems although they are fearful of a link between dieting and anorexia. The UK-origin mother of a girl who is bullied at school because of her weight explains that her elder daughter had been overweight, began dieting and verged on the anorexic. She tries to ensure that dieting does not get a high profile with her younger daughter:

> She, with my help, is watching, is trying to watch her weight. Diet – I don't like to use that word. I would never like to say diet, I think we watch what she eats, we're careful . . . I'm trying to encourage X to watch what she eats, not diet.

Another mother observes that her daughter is too embarrassed to go swimming because of her weight. She sees it as her responsibility to regulate her daughter's diet:

> Well, I would like her [to diet], 'cause she is much too much overweight so I would like her, but sensibly. I would want to be the one that was cooking for her and seeing what she was taking.

The father thinks that the problem will resolve itself when the girl gets older, 'when she's ready to lose weight, she will', when she will have the motivation to cut down on what she eats. He sees her current lack of dedication to eating less as part of being a child, unable to resist eating the things she likes. He echoes the view of other parents that it should not become an issue mainly because of a fear of eating disorders:

> ... the more you keep on to her at this age the more chance you've got they'll turn anorexic or bulimic or whatever ... she's tried to cut down, ... but she just can't resist things, that's the way kids are.

The converse problem, being underweight, is discussed by the parents of two Asian-origin boys. For the mother of one this is not an important issue; she finds it difficult to find clothes to fit him because he is so slim. He does not eat much but then, as she admits, neither does she. For the father of the other boy, his small size is more of an issue. The father clearly equates slimness with weakness, a definition which has moral rather than health or developmental overtones:

> Now we have to force him, I say you must eat one apple or banana. For him that's, I don't know, like hell to eat a banana and apple every day ... I say you're too small for your age and too little so you must eat you know, plus he's too weak, slim. To be healthy you must eat, I keep telling him.

SUMMARY POINTS

Children are far from unambiguously positive about the state of their health compared with their parents with only 34 per cent rating their health as 'good'. Parents are more likely to assess their children's health in a positive light. Mothers' or fathers' employment is not associated with perceptions of children's health and healthiness nor with children's propensity to engage in sports activities outside school.

Children (and parents) link the state of their own health to food intake and physical fitness. This suggests that children have taken on board the health messages of professionals and see health in terms of personal responsibility for the food they eat and the exercise they take.

Children also assess their lifestyles in relation to food and fitness. The practice of eating unhealthy foods is seen to be assuaged by eating healthy foods. Fitness is more of an issue for boys. Boys are much more likely to have played a sport outside school in the past week and to have visited a sports or leisure centre, with Asian-origin girls the group least likely to have done either. Girls in general are particularly critical of the format of school PE but feel that they ought to take more exercise.

Parents draw on similar themes in discussing their children's health but also refer to illness or its absence, mental wellbeing and general socialisation. The issue of encouraging children to take more exercise is especially problematic for Asian-origin mothers who fear for their children's safety outside the home and seek therefore to encourage them to stay indoors.

A key health issue for the children, especially girls, concerns the size, shape and weight of their bodies and their consequences for self-image and self-confidence.

While two-thirds of boys are happy with their bodies, only half of girls are happy. Moreover, more boys (41 per cent) are happy with their weight compared with girls (29 per cent). Over twice as many girls as boys want to lose weight (48 per cent versus 23 per cent). A small proportion, especially boys, feel they are too thin or under-sized. The dictates of fashion which emphasise the desirable social norm of slimness are clearly highly influential among girls.

Parents attribute any weight concerns of their children to genetic origins (suggesting therefore that it is difficult to find a solution), to the stages of puberty and adolescence (which will by implication pass), and to eating the wrong diet, notably junk food. In a few cases, limiting food intake is seen as part of the solution. However, parents are attuned to the dangers of dieting and a possible link with anorexia.

5. Food choices in school

This chapter focuses on the way school food decisions become part of children's self-development and increased personal responsibility when they start secondary school. Two sets of concerns emerge in particular:

- The dominance of the market ideology of choice, which is inscribed in the cafeterias of today's secondary schools, appear to offer children an array of food options which are paid for on an itemised basis and many of which are not particularly healthy.
- The concern of parents (and children) that children should have access to healthy food and be encouraged to develop healthy eating practices.

The requirements of food choice and health concerns do not necessarily work together; in practice the attractions of choosing food in the school canteen may limit children's access to a healthy diet.

CHILDREN'S DIET

In the questionnaire survey we asked the children how often they had eaten various items of food (not only in school) during the preceding week. Table 5.1 shows that children's overall diets do not consist on a daily basis of healthy foods. Almost half have not eaten wholemeal bread in the past week; only around a quarter report having eaten fresh fruit and vegetables daily. Even less say that they have eaten salad daily.

There are some differences between boys and girls (Table 5.2). For example, in their consumption of biscuits and cakes, 21 per cent of girls and 11 per cent of boys report not eating these items at all. Boys are rather more likely not to have eaten

Table 5.1   Children's reports of foods eaten in previous week: questionnaire survey

	Not at all	1–2 days	Most days	Every day
	%	%	%	%
White bread	11	25	39	25
Wholemeal bread	49	24	17	9
Chips/fried potatoes	17	51	25	7
Fresh fruit	9	30	32	29
Vegetables	14	28	35	23
Salad	30	34	21	15
Crisps	11	40	30	19
Biscuits and cakes	15	43	27	14
Sweets and chocolate	9	43	28	20
Fruit juice	10	21	32	36
Fizzy drinks	17	36	25	22

N = 521

Table 5.2   Children's reports of foods eaten in previous week by sex and by frequency: questionnaire survey

	Not at all		1–2 days		Most days		Every day	
	girls %	boys %	girls %	boys %	girls %	boys %	girls %	boys %
Wholemeal bread	47	51	29	20	17	17	7	12
Vegetables	10	17	28	29	36	34	25	20
Salad	24	35	34	33	24	19	18	13
Biscuits and cakes	21	11	43	43	23	30	12	16

N girls = 229   boys = 267

vegetables than girls (17 per cent versus 10 per cent) and also less likely to have eaten salad (35 per cent compared with 24 per cent of girls).

Overall, 10 per cent of the children are eating wholemeal bread, fresh fruit, vegetables and salad on most days, but 46 per cent report that they eat only one or none of them. A quarter (23 per cent) report eating four or five of the items from the range chips, crisps, biscuits or cakes, sweets or chocolate and fizzy drinks on most days. However, 21 per cent of children eat none of the items in this latter range.

Boys whose mothers are in full-time work consume significantly less of the chips, crisps, biscuits and cakes, sweets, chocolate and fizzy drink range of foods than do those with mothers working part-time or not at all. Indeed boys' diets vary significantly by the occupational status of parents: those boys with mothers in higher status occupations not only eat less of these foods, they eat wholemeal bread, fresh fruit, vegetables and salad more often than boys whose mothers are in lower status occupations. Similarly, boys with fathers in higher status occupations are significantly more likely to consume this range of food items than are boys with fathers in lower status occupations. For girls, the employment and occupational status of either mother or father appears to be of no relevance to their diets.

Asian-origin children report more frequent consumption of wholemeal bread, fresh fruit and vegetables than either white children or black children; there are no differences between these groups in the consumption of chips, crisps, cakes and biscuits, sweets and fizzy drinks. These findings partially support the findings of a similar study of 16-year-olds (Brannen *et al.*, 1994) but only with respect to boys.

Twenty-four per cent of the children are regularly eating wholemeal bread, fresh fruit and vegetables but avoiding the chips, crisps, cakes and biscuits, sweets and fizzy drinks. This compares with 29 per cent who are regularly eating these later foods but avoiding wholemeal bread, fresh vegetables and fresh fruit. Thirty per cent of children seem to be consuming all these foods regularly whilst 17 per cent are eating very few of them.

CHILDREN'S ASSESSMENTS OF THE HEALTHINESS OF THEIR DIETS

Less than half the children rate their diets as healthy. Nearly half say they are both healthy and unhealthy. There is little difference between boys and girls with 41 per cent of girls and 37 per cent of boys reporting their diets as very healthy or healthy (Table 5.3). Boys and girls are equally likely (48 per cent) to see their diet as mixed, both healthy and unhealthy.

We compared children's assessments of their diet with reports of what they eat. Those who frequently eat wholemeal bread, fresh fruit and vegetables and salad are

Table 5.3   Children's assessments of their diet by sex: questionnaire survey

	Girls %	Boys %
Very healthy or healthy	41	37
Healthy and unhealthy	48	48
Not very healthy	8	8
Not sure	3	6
N	246	280

significantly more likely to assess their diets as healthy compared with those who rarely eat these items ($p < .0001$). Similarly, those regularly consuming chips, crisps, cakes and biscuits, sweets and fizzy drinks are likely to rate their diet as unhealthy ($p < .05$.) This suggests that those who assess their diet as healthy are eating healthy items and basing their assessments on this fact. They are moreover discounting the importance of the unhealthy foods they eat.

SCHOOL AS A CONTEXT FOR THE CONSUMPTION OF FOOD

The school cafeteria system requires children to take responsibility for what they eat at secondary school. For those who were provided with set school meals under the old system in their middle or primary school, or for those who previously took packed lunches, dietary responsibility is significantly increased. Children can choose from a variety of types of food, snacks as well as meals.

There are opportunities to buy food at break time as well as lunch time. Those who buy nothing in the cafeteria at lunch time may be buying food at mid-morning break. Only six children in the 34 interview case studies report that they have had no mid-morning snack on the previous day at school. Fourteen have purchased a snack or crisps and nine have bought a drink (six have bought both). Seven have brought a drink or snack from home and two others have made an early start on their packed lunch. Focusing on snacks purchased in school, seven children mention crisps, five mention doughnuts or iced buns, and another five purchased sausage rolls. Only two mention that they usually eat fruit brought from home.

All three schools claim to address the subject of nutrition and healthy eating within the PSE curriculum in the children's first year at secondary school. They do so in a general way rather than specifically addressing food choices in school. However, rather few of the children in the questionnaire survey mention that the topic has been covered: 12 per cent in School 1 report that a teacher has talked to them about food and diet, 14 per cent in School 2 and 19 per cent at School 3.

Whether or not nutrition is covered in the school curriculum, any discussion on healthy eating in the school context must take account of the school's policies and practices on food within the precincts of the school. We note however that, in one school, prohibitions on specific foods and drink sold on the school premises are not related to policies to encourage healthy eating. Rather they were introduced for other reasons: drinks in glass bottles were banned on safety grounds, foods with wrappers because of problems with litter.

Dining facilities at each of the three schools differed. In one school there is a canteen which opens at break time, as well as at lunch time, and serves a limited range of snacks. In another school, year 7 pupils are provided with a separate dining room offering a limited menu of snacks with the option of going to the main school cafeteria. This school also allows an ice-cream van to park in the playground during the lunch break. A tuck shop operates on an occasional basis. The only foods prohibited by the school are chewing gum and drinks in glass bottles. The third school provides both a cafeteria and a tuck shop with a limited range of stock, for example cake and fruit, in an attempt to reduce the tide of litter which engulfs the school building by the end of each afternoon.

School lunch

In the questionnaire survey, 57 per cent of the children say that they have lunch in the cafeteria and 39 per cent take a packed lunch to school. Only five children say that they go home for lunch. As children in the first year are not generally allowed off site at lunch time, the option of going to a shop or takeaway for lunch is not generally available and only nine say that they do this. Eight children say that they have no lunch. There are differences by school. In two schools, around 60 per cent have lunch in the cafeteria and 35 per cent bring packed lunches but in the third school 50 per cent eat in the cafeteria and 48 per cent bring their own.

The questionnaire data show significant differences by sex in choice of type of lunch; 50 per cent of girls and 63 per cent of boys are having school lunch in the cafeteria (Table 5.4). Forty-six per cent of girls and only 33 per cent of boys take packed lunch. There are significant differences by ethnicity, with 50 per cent of Asian origin children eating in the cafeteria, 52 per cent of white origin, but 77 per cent of black and 84 per cent of the other children.

Table 5.4 Type of school lunch by sex and ethnicity: questionnaire survey

	Cafeteria %	Packed lunch %	Shop %	Home %	None %	N
Girls	50	46	2	1	1	249
Boys	63	33	1	1	2	283
Asian	50	43	4	3	1	110
White	52	46	1	1	2	307
Black	77	17	4	0	2	84
Other	84	16	–	–	–	25

Type of school lunch is linked to the employment status of parents, but in a surprising direction. Children whose mothers are employed are more likely to take a packed lunch to school than the children of mothers who are not working; 51 per cent of those whose mothers work full- or part-time take cafeteria lunch compared with 67 per cent of those whose mothers do not work. Of children with lone mothers, 82 per cent of those with mothers working part-time and 85 per cent of those whose mothers do not work eat in the cafeteria. This compares with 68 per cent of children whose lone mothers work full-time.

Unemployed households typically have a statutory entitlement to free school lunch for children and we therefore expected a link between eating in the school cafeteria and household unemployment. Looking only at children with neither parent in employment or one of their two parents working part-time, then 77 per cent are eating lunch in the cafeteria while 17 per cent take packed lunches, the remaining 5 per cent going to a takeaway or shop and 1 per cent having no lunch. Forty-five per cent of children from two-parent families with the mother employed eat lunch in the cafeteria and 51 per cent have packed lunch. The case studies reveal that household unemployment status is not necessarily a completely accurate indicator of take-up of free school lunches, however. In the case study households, eight children have no parent in employment but only five of them are receiving free school lunches.

In the case studies, thirteen children eat their lunch in the school cafeteria every day while ten always take packed lunch. As in the questionnaire survey, the girls in the case studies are opting for packed lunches more than the boys (10/18 girls compared with 3/15 boys). However, the case studies suggest some further complexity. Seven of the interviewees have opted for a *flexible* pattern, taking packed lunches some days and having cafeteria lunch on others. A further four, entitled to free school meals, prefer to take their own packed lunches on some days.

Content of cafeteria lunch and packed lunch

When we asked the children in the case studies what they bought at lunch time from the school cafeteria the list was short: 'pizza and chips', 'chips and fish fingers', 'beans, spaghetti, pizza and chips', 'chips or a pizza', 'chips, pizza', 'chips, crisps, pizza', and 'burgers'. None mentioned fruit or vegetables. Only one boy says that he regularly chooses the 'hot dish of the day' and three of our respondents are opting effectively for a packed lunch choosing to buy a sandwich or roll, crisps and a drink.

The range of foods in packed lunches is also limited. In the questionnaire survey we find that packed lunchers eat crisps more frequently than those eating in the cafeteria (58 per cent versus 44 per cent ate crisps on most days). There is no difference between boys' and girls' lunches. However, this practice is balanced by the more frequent consumption of chips by those eating in the cafeteria. Cakes and biscuits are also consumed most days by a greater proportion of the packed lunchers but not significantly more than those who eat in the cafeteria. Only two of the ten packed lunchers in the interview case study mention fruit as a routine constituent. A fairly standard description of a packed lunch was given by this boy:

> Mum does the sandwiches; I put my chocolate in and my packet of crisps and my drink.

We find that those children who take packed lunches report more frequent consumption of different foods from those who eat school lunch. Those bringing packed lunch are significantly more likely to eat fresh fruit and vegetables every day compared with those eating in the cafeteria: 39 per cent of girls taking packed lunch say they eat fruit every day compared with 19 per cent of those having cafeteria lunch. For boys the difference is 38 per cent versus 25 per cent. Similarly for fresh vegetables, 30 per cent of girls and 29 per cent of boys taking packed lunch eat vegetables every day compared with 19 per cent and 16 per cent of girls and boys having school dinner. There is no difference between the two groups in eating salad.

CHILDREN'S RESPONSIBILITY AND FOOD CHOICE AT SCHOOL

Children vary in the degree of responsibility with respect to eating practices at school. Some children have no scope to choose their food, taking packed lunch prepared by their mothers and having no money to spend on break-time snacks or lunch-time top-ups. Others have total control of their school-time eating practices, with money provided by parents for both break and lunch time.

The children frequently comment on the freedom of *choice* made available to them at secondary school and particularly the new opportunities at break time. These new experiences contrast with the more rigorously controlled world of primary school. The opportunity to choose their food is expressed by the children as an important part of the transition from primary to secondary school. This girl sums up her reasons for having school lunch (but only once a week) as being able to exert her freedom to choose, despite the downside of school lunch, the unhealthy food and the inconvenient cafeteria.

> I take school dinners once a week. It's my choice what day I want to have it. . . . The food is not very healthy but that's good because normally teenagers don't want healthy food . . . we're the last to go in so there's not a lot left but there is adequate food. (*And do you like to be able to choose what you have?*) Yeah. We weren't allowed to do that in my old school we were just given what was there. It's much better getting to choose your own choice.

Only one interviewee says that his reason for opting for school lunch is because he wants a 'hot' meal for his lunch and that by opting for the 'special' each day he can take advantage of a range of cooked foods. Some days he visits the ice-cream van for a hot dog:

> Cos I like a hot meal for my lunch . . . it's normally a hot meal or if it's a cold meal it will be an ice cream and a hot dog from the ice-cream van. They are different things, there's chips and curry, fish and chips, steak and kidney pie.

While children (and some parents) subscribe to the ideology of choice, many children do not exercise food choices in practice. A boy, on free school meals, praises the range of meals available estimating that there are about ten different foods to choose from at lunchtime. In practice he opts almost every day for two slices of pizza and a drink. Not taking advantage of the range of food on offer is not uncommon:

> I eat that every day. (*Every single day you have chips and fish fingers?*) Yeah. (*You never get bored with it?*) I like chips but sometimes fish fingers are not that good.

> On the induction day I had sausage roll, pastie and chips and it was really nice. So I got pastie and chips ever since.

Interestingly, the advocates of packed lunches use the converse argument of the lack of choice available in the canteen. Some say that, if they eat in the cafeteria every day they end up buying burgers and chips; one girl says that she likes to have school lunch but she knows that she will buy chips every day. These children seek therefore to be saved from their own choices by having a packed lunch provided. Children critical of the school cafeteria apply a *health perspective* in making decisions about what kind of foods and type of lunch to eat:

> Well, like it's good but they could do more healthy meals because it's all burgers and chips and that . . . (*You think it's a bit unhealthy?*) Well, it's all right but it's not very good if you keep on eating burgers every day.

> I prefer [packed lunch] yes, but I would like to have school dinners. But I reckon it's healthier having a packed lunch cos at school dinners I would be buying chips, I would, everyday and hamburgers and stuff.

Children's food preferences also have a bearing on their choice of school lunch. Overall, 7 per cent of the questionnaire survey sample are vegetarian, 25 per cent restrict the type of meat they eat and 68 per cent eat all types of meat. Of the children in the case studies, four are strict vegetarian, 13 have restricted-meat diets, and 16 are unrestricted in their meat eating. Certainly vegetarians report limited variety of foods available at school. Indeed the lack of choice influences many to bring their own packed lunches.

SPENDING MONEY IN THE SCHOOL CAFETERIA

Twelve of the 34 case study interviewees are given money by their parents for their lunch in the school cafeteria every day and a further five are entitled to a free lunch voucher with a current value of £1.10. Of the regular lunchers, three are given less than the value of a free lunch, one girl receiving 80p and the other two having £1 each. Five interviewees have between £1.20 and £1.50 to spend and four have £2. Children note that their lunch money is variable both in amount and what it is meant to cover. In some cases, pocket money is being used to supplement lunch or break time, in only one case is spending the other way round.

Most of the children are positive about the practice of spending their money in the school cafeteria and about the food they can buy there. One girl on free school lunches is, however, critical and has mixed feelings about what she can get. Of the six with a flexible lunch pattern, buying their lunch some days, taking packed lunch on others, one expresses mixed feelings and one is negative about the food available at school.

When we asked about children's satisfaction with the amount of money they have to spend in the canteen, seven children say they are happy and can buy what they want. Of these, one is getting £1.50 and three £2 to spend on lunch; one is on free school meals and two are getting less than £1.10. Of the six who accept what they can buy (as opposed to being happy with it), three are on free school meals and two are getting more than £1.10 and one less than that. Of those who express mixed feelings, one is on free school meals and two are getting over £1.10. Nine say that they think the food expensive.

Deciding how to apportion money is a new experience for many of the children. Balancing the cost of the items selected is, from the descriptions given by the children, more important than balancing their diet in health terms. As this boy explains:

I spend 20p at break time and keep £1.30. Sometimes I get burger and chips or sometimes just get chips, a drink and a chocolate bar.

Several children mention taking money from their own spending money to buy additional snacks at break time or to supplement their lunches. One child, getting £1.20 a day, sees the cafeteria as expensive and plans to use her pocket money to supplement her spending at school. She sees this as beginning to exert her independence and 'making her own way'.

MOTHERS' INFLUENCE UPON CHILDREN'S SCHOOL FOOD DECISIONS

The case studies highlight a range of ways in which mothers influence what children eat when they are at school. The degree of responsibility which mothers allocate to their children varies considerably with some mothers allowing their children considerable autonomy, letting them use the school cafeteria and providing them with money. The children are able to make completely free choices about what they eat at school within the options available. Other mothers keep tight control over the content of the packed lunches and refuse to provide money for additional snacks.

Mothers who take a relaxed view

A common viewpoint held by mothers was that what happens at school with regard to food is peripheral to their children's wellbeing. Mothers consider that the food they provide at home compensates adequately for what the children consume outside.

> Because whatever we give her in early morning or in the evening we know that we are giving her enough, even if she didn't have enough at lunchtime.

> I told them that this year I was going to give them a proper lunch – a packed lunch – again, because it was hot dogs, it was silly things, it was rubbish, also they came in starving but I cook properly and I give them vitamin C.

Only three mothers express the view that they rely, albeit only sometimes, upon their child having a meal at school. Two mothers say that they like their daughters, both on free school meals, to have a hot meal at lunchtime although both girls prefer packed lunches. One working mother says that sometimes the school lunch is her daughter's main meal of the day.

Many parents whose children eat in the cafeteria do not know exactly what their child eats at school. One lone mother says that she has given up asking, another indicated that she had not really thought about what her son eats at school. However, some mothers know, and many suspect, that their children are eating foods they consider to be unhealthy. If they know their children are also eating 'proper' food, they may feel reassured. As the children also see it, healthy eating can counteract unhealthy food consumption. In the following case the son is positively perceived by his mother because he tells her both the good and the bad news about his diet. Moreover, she is able to excuse her son for giving in to the temptations of the ice-cream van, parked every day in the school playground.

> He will have what they call the 'special'. It's a proper meal not chips and chips, I mean then he will go and have his ice-cream. But if they have an ice-cream van there at the school it's very hard for a 12-year-old.

Food choice as an educational device

Parents acknowledge that their children may not want to be tied to eating exactly the same quantity and type of food every day. Learning to take advantage of the freedom to choose and to negotiate financial transactions are seen as an essential part of growing up. In this sense, giving children school-lunch money is an educational device. The development of personal preferences and taking personal responsibility are processes which some parents seek to foster.

> My wife and I have got misgivings about what it is they're eating but again it's part of growing up. Parents have to start accepting that they will eat what they want to eat.

> That is for her to decide ... I think it's time a girl of 12 chose her own lunch, and what she likes, and got some value for money.

These types of comments reflect an endorsement of the developmental paradigm by which processes children are supposed to develop into adults. But parents may also place importance on children being socialised in market values referred to in the latter remark – 'got some value for money'.

Mothers who take control

Mothers who give their children packed lunches do so in order that they may 'know' what their children eat. However, these mothers may give in to requests to provide money for cafeteria lunch or for spending at mid-morning break – crisps or drinks to supplement packed lunch. They recognise that the money goes on what they regard to be junk food but are prepared to condone this on the grounds that unhealthy food will be offset by the healthy food provided at home. This is part of a strategy whereby mothers give children an incentive to continue having packed lunch.

The mothers who maintain the greatest influence over their children's diet are two whose daughters have weight problems; they both admit that they have adopted the strategy of packed lunch to keep a reign on their daughters' food intake. Given the opportunity to eat at school, both girls are eating what the mothers feel to be the wrong foods.

> I can monitor what she eats because she's on the weighty side and that was one of the reasons she was being bullied . . . so I can *see* [our emphasis] what she is eating because I found when I was giving her money to have a school lunch she was eating all the wrong things. It was sausage rolls everyday, you know . . . talk about high calories, so I like to, at least I *know* what I give her to eat.

> Really and honestly the reason was because they were getting so fat cause they love school dinners and I decided no, I'll make packed lunches for them then I'd *know* [our emphasis] what they have and they can have a meal at nights.

SUMMARY POINTS

School meals in secondary school, organised on the cafeteria system, are based on the principles of food choice and payment on an itemised basis. Children are introduced to increased responsibility for their diets when they start secondary school and find it an attractive feature of the change from primary to secondary school. Parents give credence to the importance of children learning to discriminate and to make decisions about which foods to buy and children endorse the notion of food choice even though they do not always exercise it. Many children alternate use of the canteen, which they often consider a treat, with taking packed lunches. Most packed-lunch children buy or bring snack foods as well.

While some mothers legitimate children making food choices in the cafeteria as an educational device, others adopt a relaxed approach giving in to children's demand to spend money in the canteen and to their refusal to eat 'boring sandwiches' every day. Some adopt a flexible strategy of allowing children to buy food one or two days a week in order to achieve some balance in their children's diet. Parents reassure themselves that an unhealthy diet at school is counteracted by a healthy diet provided at home. Children also subscribe to the notion of unhealthy food cancelling out the intake of unhealthy foods. Yet other parents try to maintain control over their children's diet by a packed lunch regime.

Food options provided in schools tend towards the 'junk' end of the dietary continuum and provide limited choice, especially for vegetarians; most children try to stretch their money to cover drinks and snacks as well as lunch and few have the resources to cover all of these. Compared with those eating school lunch, those taking packed lunch report a higher consumption of wholemeal bread, fresh fruit and vegetables compared with those eating in the cafeteria. However those having packed lunch also report a higher consumption of crisps and chocolate bars which are brought from home or purchased in the cafeteria. Boys are more likely than girls to eat in the school cafeteria.

Children's assessments of their diet are entirely realistic, with half saying their diet is both healthy and unhealthy. Both parents and children are critical of the health aspects of school food although many parents do not know what their children eat and have difficulty finding out from their children. Vegetarian children are particularly critical of the canteen food available. Mothers often discount the food children eat at school on the grounds that they provide a 'proper' diet at home which compensates for the deficiencies at school. Only a minority of parents say that children's diet at school is a crucial element of their nutrition.

Children's diet is influenced by household employment and by mothers' employment. Children of full-time employed mothers are more, rather than less, likely to take a packed lunch to school, a practice associated with a higher intake of wholemeal bread, fresh fruit and vegetables. Boys, but not girls, whose mothers are employed full-time eat significantly less from the range of foods including chips, crisps, cakes and biscuits, sweets and fizzy drinks, than those whose mothers are part-time or not employed. Asian-origin boys eat wholemeal bread, fresh fruit and vegetables more often than their white peers.

6. Sex and puberty

The transition to secondary school directly parallels the onset of puberty which occurs, for girls, around 12 years of age. This chapter examines patterns of household discussion concerning matters to do with sex and puberty and the part played by mothers, fathers and others in sex education, and the factors which affect discussion. It identifies different patterns of household communication and it ends with a consideration of the effects of parents' own experience in childhood of such discussion with their own parents.

SOURCES OF INFORMATION: SEX AND PUBERTY

For children, knowledge about sex and growing up comes from a variety of sources, not just from the home. These topics are dealt with formally at school and, informally, in discussion with friends, since peers are for many children a prime source of information. In the questionnaire survey we asked the children two separate questions: first, since starting secondary school, if they have talked to anyone about changes in their body and worries concerning sex; and second, if, in the same period, parents, teachers or friends have talked to them about sex. We asked the interview case-study children if they have any worries about puberty and if they have talked to their parents about puberty. We asked more detailed questions of the parents, if they have talked about puberty, sex, reproduction, contraception, AIDS and sexually transmitted diseases with their children.

The questionnaire data show girls are more likely to report parents and teachers talking to them about sex, boys more likely to report friends (Table 6.1). A high proportion of boys (58 per cent) report that they have talked to no one about worries about puberty compared with 38 per cent of girls. Overall, over a third (38 per cent) of both boys and girls, report that no one has spoken to them about sex.

Significantly more 12-year-olds report having discussed sex with their parents compared with 16-year-olds (Brannen *et al.*, 1994), with girls significantly more likely to do so than boys. Conversely, more 16-year-olds report discussion of sex with teachers than do 12-year-olds, while discussion with friends is roughly similar for both groups.

The role of the school

Table 6.1 suggests that teachers play only a minimal role compared with parents and friends. By the end of the first year in secondary school – the period covered in the case studies – puberty has been addressed at school for most of the girls if not for boys, with 15 of the 18 girls and 10 of the 16 boys in the case studies reporting that the topics have been covered. Six of the nine claiming not to have covered puberty at school are at the same school, suggesting that there has been no coverage or that it has been so minimal as to be unmemorable. Two UK-origin girls, from different schools, describe their diverse experiences at school; the first gives an account of very comprehensive formal sex education at school while the second account suggests a more cursory approach by the school:

Table 6.1 Percentages talking to and being talked to by parents, teachers and friends about sex and puberty by child's sex and ethnicity and mothers' employment: questionnaire survey

						Mothers' employment		
	Girls %	Boys %	Asian %	White %	Black %	Full-time %	Part-time %	Not in work %
Talked to about sex								
by parents	36	29	28	38	22	34	30	32
by teachers	14	9	8	12	13	15	9	11
by friends	30	33	24	31	42	36	29	30
by no one	37	38	49	33	32	34	42	37
Talked about worries about sex								
to mother	23	19	17	23	24	20	25	17
to father	2	10	6	8	3	6	8	4
to teachers	–	1	1	–	1	–	–	1
to friends	19	17	13	17	27	20	18	17
to no one	62	63	69	62	51	64	60	64
Talked about worries about puberty								
to mother	52	28	41	42	28	43	42	33
to father	3	15	8	11	8	9	11	8
to teachers	[1]	[1]	[1]	–	–	[1]	[1]	–
to friends	14	9	10	11	15	13	10	11
to no one	38	58	51	45	55	45	46	55
N	236	262	104	288	77	162	166	170

[ ] indicates number not percentage

In secondary school we had a nurse come to the school and talk to only the girls about periods and the boys had a wet dreams talk. We had sex education in primary school but we had the period talk in secondary school.

Well, like, in one of our PE lessons us girls had a lesson on periods and that but that's about it.

The role of friends

Table 6.1 suggests that the role of friends is not significantly different for boys than for girls. Certainly, more children report talking with their friends about these subjects than with their teachers but not as much as they do with parents.

The case studies highlight the role of friends as sounding boards and as enablers in the sharing of experience and worries about sex rather than the more technical advice given by teachers and parents. However, children in this age group may not have a great need for friends as confidants on these subjects, unlike the older adolescents. For some boys, sex and puberty may not yet be relevant. One Asian boy reports that he does not talk to his friends about puberty because 'they're usually interested in computer games'.

The role of parents

Table 6.1 shows the greater contribution of parents than teachers or friends as sources of information on these topics. Girls are more likely than boys to report that one or both parents have talked to them about sex: 36 per cent of girls compared with 29 per cent of boys. With regard to talking to parents about worries about puberty, boys are significantly more likely than girls to have discussed these with their fathers. Over half the girls (52 per cent) but 28 per cent of boys report that they have talked to their mothers about worries about puberty. This compares with the more limited role of fathers – 15 per cent of boys and 3 per cent of girls report talking to fathers about puberty.

There are significant differences for girls by mothers' employment. Those whose mothers work full-time outside the home are significantly more likely to report that they have talked to their mothers about changes in their bodies than are those whose mothers are not working (56 per cent versus 45 per cent, Table 6.2). Differences for boys are not significant.

There are differences by household composition according to the presence or not of resident fathers. Girls living with lone mothers are significantly more likely to report talking about sex with their mothers: 38 per cent compared with 21 per cent of those who live with both parents. Boys too, living with lone mothers, are more likely to report themselves as talking to them about sex (28 per cent) as against 17 per cent who live with both parents.

Table 6.2   Talking to mothers about body changes and sex by mothers' employment, household composition and sex: questionnaire data

| | Mothers' employment | | | | |
	Full-time %	Part-time %	Not working %	Both parents %	Lone mother %
Talked to mother about puberty					
girls	56	51	45	53	49
boys	31	30	23	27	33
Talked to mother about worries about sex					
girls	21	29	21	21	38
boys	19	22	15	17	28
N (girls)	81	77	78	179	37
N (boys)	82	89	92	181	46

Table 6.1 also shows the differences by ethnic group with more discourse on sex but not puberty between white parents and children than between children and their Asian-origin parents. By and large black children report even lower levels of communication.

In the case studies we asked about the same topics as in the questionnaire survey. More discourse is reported between mothers and children and less between fathers and children than in the questionnaire. However, since over 40 per cent of the case study households have no resident father, less interaction is not unexpected. Almost all girls (16 out of 18) report that puberty has been talked about at home, while only a minority of boys (5/16) say this. Five mothers and two fathers report that they have talked to their sons but only two of the sons report that this is so. Attempts described by four mothers to cover puberty, sex, contraception and AIDS with their sons apparently have failed since the sons admit no conversations in their interviews. This constitutes a significant divergence of opinion since several of the mothers describe having detailed discussions and suggests that the sons have chosen to ignore what was said or found the content of these talks so irrelevant to them that they dismissed them.

Twelve case-study mothers report having talked about puberty to their daughters but only six claim to have talked about sex and eight about contraception. Five mothers, but no fathers, say they have talked to sons about puberty and most of these mothers claim to have covered sex and contraception as well. However, whilst girls are having more discussion or input from their mothers than boys, much of this extra input is focused on menstruation, a topic forced by nature on to the agenda in the case of girls. As in the questionnaire survey, the case-study lone mothers are more likely to discuss these matters with their sons than are mothers in two-parent households.

FACTORS INFLUENCING THE DISCUSSION OF SEX EDUCATION IN THE HOUSEHOLD

Sex of parent, sex of child, household composition and the cultural origins of the family are key dimensions influencing the ways in which sex education is conducted and constructed as a topic of discourse within households. With 12-year-old girls there is an urgent need for mothers to discuss menstruation. For boys the matter is less pressing; the subject may be safely postponed until later, if not indefinitely, since the onset of male maturity is more gradual and less dramatic.

Children living with lone mothers are more likely to have had some sex education, compared with those living in two-parent households. Lone mothers of sons in our study are trying, consciously or unconsciously, to compensate for the input that a resident father might have provided. However, lone mothers may be overestimating the possible input of a resident father. While mothers think that fathers are better able to talk to boys about their development and about sex, fathers, it seems, are rather reluctant.

A UK-origin working mother explains how she left it to her husband:

I must admit I left it up to my husband with the boys because I thought it might be easier, but now I don't know really, I think they learned more from school than they got from him.

The father admits that his son has learnt from his elder brother or from school:

I have to admit I don't think I've talked to him about puberty and sex, partly because ... he's well aware of seeing his elder brother develop and so he's probably aware of things second hand ... and I think sex and reproduction were probably tackled at the school at an earlier age than we perceived ... I think we became aware that some of the work that probably should have been done by us had been done by his school earlier.

Ethnic origin is also a critical determinant concerning whether or not matters of sex and puberty are discussed. For some of the Asian-origin parents the subject causes no problems since, where it is culturally taboo, it is totally avoided. However, other Asian-origin mothers accept that their children are living in a very different culture from the one in which they themselves grew up and that they must address these problems or at least ensure that someone else teaches their child the necessary facts. This mother differs from many Asian-origin mothers since she is divorced and has previously worked full-time. She explains how she would *like* to talk to her children, stressing the absence of their father but how she relies on other members of the family because they have been to school in the UK and therefore have a different attitude and approach to discussing sexuality.

> I'm actually shy to tell them because I'm a lady, yeah ... my family's children, brother, sister, they've all been to school in this country, except me. So my sister, she's really open-minded, so she wouldn't mind to tell anything ... sometimes I love to tell them, now I'm getting better. I say don't be shy, I'm your mother, I'm your friend as well. Cos we don't have a man in this house, so you know I should tell them.

Although employment may broaden women's horizons and influence their educative role concerning their children's sex education we only found evidence of this with respect to discussing puberty (see Table 6.2). Girls whose mothers work full-time are more likely to talk to mothers about puberty. Moreover, when maternal employment is considered in relation to ethnicity, we find no differences.

PARENTS' APPROACHES TO THE DISCUSSION OF SEX AND PUBERTY

In the case studies, households are classified according to three patterns of discussion:

- non-discursive households – in which parents report that the topics of sex and puberty have not, and will not, be raised;
- potentially discursive households – in which the parents intend to cover these subjects when they perceive the child to be 'ready' or where they intend that some other household member such as a sibling, will assume the responsibility;
- discursive households – in which communication is underway to varying degrees.

Non-discursive households

Of the seven households in this group, six are Asian-origin and in only one does the mother work full-time. In the two households with girls, both Muslim – one from Bangladesh and the other of East African Asian origin – the daughters report no dialogue with their mother about puberty. Both mothers are widowed and have never worked outside the home since coming to the UK. The Bangladeshi-origin daughter says 'These things would never be discussed', a view confirmed by her 21-year-old sister who acted as interpreter in the interview with her mother:

> They never told me as well because they are really shy about this sort of stuff ... back home, nobody teaches anything back home. We have to learn when you get married.

Among the five households with boys, where parents and children both agree that nothing has been said, four are of Asian origin and one of UK origin. One of the Asian-origin mothers who works full-time as a stock checker rationalises her passive role, that her son will absorb all the information he needs from a variety of sources external to the household, notably school, books and television:

> They pick up information from school and from outside, from television ... there's

so many books and leaflets and so many things on television these days that they find out automatically.

A non-employed widowed mother of Asian origin reports that she feels that her son should be told about these things by *teachers* but not by herself, but currently considers him 'too young'. Her view is that the right age for him to be told was 'when he's 18 or 21'. The only UK-origin mother in this group has twin sons; she says they get silly if she tries to talk to them so she has not persevered.

Potentially discursive households

This group of five households includes two Asian-origin girls, a pair of UK-origin twin girls, and two UK-origin boys. Like the Asian-origin mother in the previous section, the UK-origin parents of the boys rely on their sons 'picking up' their information on sex. In this case, the 'picking up' occurs within the household namely through older siblings. In one case the parents indicate that they have invested considerable energy providing technical information. The father reports '... books on the facts of life from an age where they are far too young to understand emotional things.' The mother has not spoken directly to her younger son, assuming that he is 'soaking things up' from other family members. A second UK-origin boy with a lone working mother describes a similar situation – 'she knows that I know it, having older brothers'.

The following Asian-origin family arrives at the same situation, with an older sibling conveying the information but, in this case, because the parents feel unable to cope with it themselves. The mother explains how contact with the school health service at a routine health check at primary school alerted her to her role in educating her daughter. However, she off-loaded the responsibility on to her older, 18-year-old daughter:

> If I hadn't had the hint from the doctor that it is our job then I would have left it to her schoolteacher ... the doctor in the clinic told me to explain to her everything about the periods and things like that you know. Cos I was brought up that we don't discuss things like that with children. So I would not like to, so it is better for [the older daughter] to.

Presumably the older daughter has received all her sex education at school or from friends.

A non-employed, UK-origin mother with twin daughters reports that 'I talk to my girls about periods, I've never kept it a secret from them'. However, she is really waiting for the 'questions to come' from her daughters rather than raising the issues herself. She tries to empower them by creating the opening.

> Puberty yes, sex no. Reproduction sort of. Contraception no ... AIDS, no. We haven't really touched on that or the sexually transmitted diseases ... I think as the time goes by and questions will arise. Yes it will be talked about then.

Her two daughters when asked if they will discuss periods and things with their parents, one says 'probably with her mum', the other doubts if she will talk to either parent.

An Asian-origin father whose employed wife has dealt with puberty with their daughter explains how he expects (or intends) to take a role in sex education when it comes to AIDS and sexually transmitted diseases. He acknowledges that his daughter feels freer to talk with his wife when he is not there, but he sees himself as backing up his wife. The school takes the lead role in providing sex education whilst his wife answers any questions when they arise. When the time comes to discuss AIDS and sexually transmitted diseases, he intends to use the standard middle-class approach of supplying the literature.

> ... my wife obviously will talk to me if there is any problem or something, seek my advice on it or something, but otherwise I think [the daughter] knows enough. She is getting the education or whatever, taught at school, and she asks her questions, she sits down there, and then asks probably, um, while I'm not here, then [the wife] talks straight to me that she was talking about it ... [AIDS and sexually transmitted diseases]. I think I may deal with her personally, I may try to explain to her later, may give her something to read about, rather than talk and see what you think. I'd say 'This is interesting, have a read of it.'

Discursive households

It is more difficult to convey the extent and meaning of discussion with respect to this group of 12 households (seven of the 31 households have not been allocated in the analysis since information was not available from both a parent and children). Some parents say they are covering the topics fully but it sounds as if they are using the words – sex, condoms, AIDS – but are not actually providing any real explanations for the children. The approach can be epitomised as 'the jigsaw method': that is if enough small pieces of information are supplied to the child, then he or she will eventually, by deduction, grasp what the total picture looks like. Few households bring together all the pieces to form a coherent explanation.

Some parents in these households provide a wide range of technical information in the form of literature to the children. Some of their children acknowledge this supply of information, while others do not. Other households report an ad hoc approach, supplying some pieces of the puzzle but declining to provide the others. They skirt around the tricky topics of sex but are able to talk about AIDS and contraception, principally when these topics are raised in the home by television or newspaper articles.

In the following interview extracts from the case studies, neither mother suggests to the interviewer that there is any inconsistency here, namely that contraception and AIDS cannot be discussed without addressing the 'nuts and bolts' of sex. The first mother describes talking to her daughter, how they have discussed AIDS but not sexually transmitted diseases. Sex is dealt with solely in terms of morality:

> Probably not so much the sexually transmitted diseases, probably touched upon it because we have talked about AIDS and everything. (*Have you discussed things like periods with her?*) Oh yeah at length. (*And would you have discussed sex itself with her or not really?*) Not the actual function of sex or whatever, but we have sort of talked about it in general terms in as much that it's something that you don't do unless you really love somebody and care for somebody and it's, you know, along those sort of lines ... but it's not what I would call the nuts and bolts of sex as such unless she has asked me a particular question.

The other mother reports providing or supplementing topics sparked off by classwork at school:

> (*And sex itself have you discussed that?*) No, not really to be honest, not actual sex itself, I haven't. (*Reproduction?*) Yes, sort of, because they had someone come round the school and we did chat about that then. (*Contraception?*) Yes, yes. (*You*

have talked about that?) Yes, she actually was telling me about the women's, like a cap.

The father in this latter household expresses strong feelings about dealing with questions from his children, again mentioning the importance of waiting for the moment when the child asks.

> We've always waited until the kids have asked us and if they ask us a specific question then we'll give them a full and specific answer. There's no cutting corners or brushing it under the carpet . . . if they ask a question they get a proper answer.

The father's approach squares with the jigsaw method suggested in his wife's account, dealing with the specific question about the contraceptives without actually getting to grips with the unasked questions about sex.

By contrast, the lone mothers in this group adopt saturation techniques but with varying degrees of success. A nursing home inspector with two sons describes her approach, not waiting for the question to be asked by her son but pushing literature and placing considerable reliance on the media, particularly the television. She feels that her work in a health-related field has made her more able to deal with these subjects. In this case the son's early onset of puberty is probably also significant:

> I give, as I did with [the older son] and I do with [the target son], . . . encourage them to read literature. I sometimes bring them home, selecting what I thought might be useful for them to sit and look at and to read when they're sat next to me. So it's *not forbidden* [our emphasis]. And I do talk to [the son] about puberty and his voice is breaking now anyway, quite noticeably, which is earlier than his friends. None of his friends are going through that. So he's obviously a bit *more hormonally advanced* than they are. So he needed to talk about it. I've talked about girls' menstrual cycles and things like that and talked about contraception. (*And on what kind of occasions have these sort of things been discussed?*) Following things on television, maybe programmes about them on television.

However, the son, whilst appreciating his mother's candour, admits to inhibitions in speaking to her, preferring to talk to his friend. He acknowledges that the subject is not difficult for his mother; he sees the problem as being his:

> It's not embarrassing to my mum. She says that I can go and ask her anything . . . I find it embarrassing. (*So what friends would you talk to about things like that?*) A boy in my class, friends in my class.

The interchange between mother and son is therefore not two-way. The model of communication may be imperfect but the boy receives sound factual information from his mother.

Another UK-origin, non-working lone mother describes similar attempts to supply her eldest son with the facts but has to contend with her son's bored response:

> Puberty, sex, reproduction, contraceptive, as far as condoms are concerned. I tried to explain the pill to him, but he didn't . . . he was getting bored with that, so I didn't bother. AIDS, yeah, I've spoken about that, and sexually transmitted diseases. More AIDS than any others. Like we did talk a bit about thrush and things like that, but the same as when we were talking about, what was it, the contraceptive. It's a case of it wasn't going in. He was taking so much in but he was getting bored with it, so, like I left it. But he's had talks in school since. And

like I probably will get the books out again. I might go through them again, or just leave them for him to read.

Sadly her son was one of the ones who declined to recall any of this in his interview. His apparent lack of interest and boredom during her attempts may have been genuine or perhaps a mask for his embarrassment.

A UK-origin lone mother who works full-time as a secretary describes discussing sex with her only child. They are the only case in which child and mother both agree that most aspects of sex and puberty have been covered in considerable depth. The mother has clearly reflected a great deal on how to approach the subject and its many aspects. She refers to the embarrassment which sex causes for parents and children. She adopts the 'sex is part of life' approach and is cognisant of the harsh environment in which they live (a particularly tough council estate). The mother does not duck any of the issues and describes talking to her daughter at an early age. She acknowledges that her daughter may have reservations about asking questions and that she, the mother, must raise issues. She compares her 'nuts and bolts' approach with explanations concerning putting the key in the electricity meter. She makes use of books and does not avoid the question that feelings accompany sex. Even so, she is anxious to stress that she has not yet covered everything but intends to, again at the appropriate 'time':

I have struggled with this from when [the daughter] was about, well whatever age, I suppose it was about eightish. Yeah, the actual mechanics. I mean you can dance around the subject, at some point you have got to have some illustration of what goes where and I mean most parents find that extremely difficult. (*Why do you think that parents find it so difficult?*) I suppose it's embarrassing in a way. I mean sex is still loaded with embarrassment and shame in many ways and you are almost initiating them into something. That's the way I received it when I was young, that you are being given information that you will immediately go out and act on, and I have obviously, I have thought about it a great deal. I have got books out of the library, consulted friends and realised the only way was to do it in conjunction with the school and that when [the daughter] asked me questions ... But she didn't actually because I don't think she wanted to. Children also feel in some respects a bit reserved about asking questions and things. But I steeled myself to approach it, just how I would explain how to put the key in the electricity meter so that you can have electricity, and what happens when you have periods. All that's got to be done, and it's got to be done at a fairly early age, and more so today. They handled it extremely well at the junior school started them off on sex education, and I had one or two little goes with her saying 'We have got a book', and (would) look through (it) and say 'Do you know this and what about that?' and tackled it just like a learning of anything else, without any –. I don't think I showed embarrassment. (I told her) 'This is what will happen.' I started off from the angle of periods and that you will change as you get older. I think we have covered AIDS and things like that, venereal diseases. We have got a transvestite who lives on this floor, I mean we have been through that. But her own feelings, dealing with it on a one-to-one basis, her own feelings how she would be dealing with her sexuality and mine, having to deal with it face to face. Masturbating, things like that. Most parents find that quite difficult – you either lie, or you tell the truth, then you have to kind of think, well. My approach is that we are talking about life. We are doing life here and this is what people do. This is what people are and there is good behaviour and there is bad behaviour and very clearly it's important now to get over to young people, not the shame and the doing naughty things, but keeping yourself safe and not endangering yourself ... There is quite a lot of ground still to be covered, but I think her questions will come and, you know there is a time, you get the clues, don't you, when they start talking about boys perhaps more.

PARENTS' OWN EXPERIENCES OF PARENTAL SEX EDUCATION

Only two of the 13 fathers in the case studies reported that their parents had talked to them about sex or puberty, one of Asian origin and one of UK origin. Both fathers of boys, they claim to have talked about sex and reproduction with their own sons. By contrast, seven out of 16 UK-origin mothers and one out of nine Asian-origin mothers interviewed, report that their mothers had talked to them about sex and puberty. An Indian-origin mother describes the very basic information she received from her mother in the context of cultural taboos and a heavy reliance on schools as sources of scientific information:

> Well, yes as far as I can remember, my mum she did tell us before we started our periods like you know. Then she told us, your breasts start growing and you get the periods this is what you have to do. Yes, change of the body she did talk to us, but the rest we learned in school.

The lone mother who has been most open with her daughter, quoted at length in the section 'Discursive households' above, recalls how her mother made sure she was well-prepared for periods but steered clear of the tricky subject of sex:

> I think my mum gave me a talk about periods because she had started menstruating without her mum ever having told her that it was going to happen. So she was very worried when that happened ... it wasn't explained, it's never the things you need to know really. But that was just because they didn't want me to know because I wasn't supposed to be doing it, so there was no great detail in fact. It was all very sketchy.

Several mothers describe what was probably a common experience with the school providing all the sex education and no discussion at home:

> Minimal description of what periods were. That's all I remember. And it was, there was a – I think a note had gone home that we were having the sex education thing, and I think she asked me whether we had had it and I said 'Yes', and she said 'Thank goodness'.

A UK-origin mother who works full-time as a district nurse, a factor she sees as significant, explains her concerns in telling her sons and daughter about sex and how her own mother had neglected to tell her anything.

> I don't want to leave it too late but then you don't want to start it too early. We have always called whatever part of the body it is by that name. I suppose that's being a nurse ... In fact I didn't know anything until it all started. I was staying with my godmother and I heard afterwards that she told my mother off. No, I didn't know anything about it. I think that's partly why I want mine to know what's going on.

Several UK-origin mothers told stories with a similar thread concerning being unprepared by their mothers particularly with regard to menstruation, such that they had made a point of addressing the subjects with their daughters. This Asian-origin mother tells of her anger that she had been kept in the dark by her parents' 'shyness' about sex. Although she finds it difficult, she feels that her children should have the necessary information and has enlisted the help of her younger, more westernised sister:

> When I had my first child I was totally new for that, I didn't know how to give birth to a child ... So then I come angry sometimes, why our parents never tell, they all shy, they think it's not good to tell to your children, you know.

Another mother (of UK origin) says that the problem had more to do with her own embarrassment as a child which prevented her from encouraging her own mother to pursue the matter:

> No, I mean I can remember my mum saying to me, 'Are you having sex classes at school?' And I said 'Yes,' and she went 'Oh that's good, if there is anything you want to ask me feel free,' but it was sort of said in a way where it was 'Well you are being taught in school so there shouldn't be anything you need to ask me.' ... not because she was prudish or I don't think it was because she got particularly embarrassed. I think it was probably me that felt more embarrassed than her actually. So I didn't really, I never really asked her about anything.

However, in dealing with her own children, this mother says she finds it much easier especially since she has the resources of the media to support her. Like other mothers, she talks about 'sitting down' to talk to her children, a phrase which signifies raising important subjects. She is moreover ambivalent about 'sitting down' to talk about sex with her children; she is afraid that by making too much of the issues she may put her children off the discussion altogether:

> The programmes that they see they will sort of ask questions about it like that and you discuss things. It's probably something I wouldn't *sit down* and talk to them about unless they asked me a question or whatever. But I think certainly [the daughter] is much more able to talk to me about those things than I was able to talk to my mother.

However, her daughter reiterates many of the points her mother made about her relationship with her own mother; rather she says she prefers to talk to her cousins about sex and 'that sort of thing', especially now that she is 'older':

> I am all right talking about puberty and that because I have already learned that subject at school sort of thing. So while I was in Middle School I was talking to my mum about that, how was it all going to start and all that. But now I am older and like I have grown more aware of what I am going to say to my mum sort of thing, we don't talk about that sort of thing ... I know enough, that's going to see me through it. And I have got quite a few of my cousins, my younger cousin who is going up to High School has started sort of thing. If I had started now, I would have talked to them quite a bit about it, about what's going to happen sort of thing.

SUMMARY POINTS

Since the onset of puberty for many children coincides with starting secondary school, school induction programmes and PSE curricula in the first year of secondary school need to take explicit account of this. In this study, parents constitute the most significant source of information concerning sex and puberty followed by friends; teachers are the least significant.

Factors affecting discussion on these issues include sex of child, sex of parent, mothers' employment status, household composition and ethnic origin:

- Boys report less communication from any source – parents, teachers and friends – while girls report more discussion. With respect to puberty, more than half of boys talk to no one; nearly two-thirds of both boys and girls had talked to no one about sex.
- Sex and household status of parent is also significant. Mothers, especially lone mothers, report considerable discussion with children about sex while fathers are much less significant.
- Full-time employed mothers are significantly more likely to talk about menstruation to daughters according to their own reports especially compared with non-employed mothers, but with no differences on sex education.
- Ethnic origin of parent is significant, with Asian-origin and black parents reported by their children to have had less discussion concerning sex (but not puberty) compared with white UK-origin parents; some Asian-origin case study parents are unlikely ever to raise issues with children to do with sex because of cultural taboos. Others engage other kin members to impart the relevant information to their children or rely on teachers.

Three patterns of household discussion concerning sex and puberty are identified:

- *non-discursive households* where there is an assumption that someone outside the household will provide the information, namely teachers or kin; these households regard sex as a taboo subject largely for cultural reasons;
- *potentially discursive households* where the children are considered to be not yet 'ready' (e.g. girls may not have started to menstruate) or where instruction or example are thought to be provided by others in the household: for example one parent thinks the other parent has or will provide sex education or an elder sibling is presumed to have imparted the information;
- *discursive households* which fall along a continuum; typical is the parent with the 'jigsaw approach' in which she give bits of information but neglects to talk about the 'nuts and bolts' of sex so that overall, coherent explanations are not provided for the children.

Parents report that critical to the discussion of sex in the household is the child's attitude and behaviour in seeking information and in initiating discussion of the topic. Parents place importance upon waiting for the 'right moment' to talk in a relaxed way to their children (without overkill or putting them off) and the right moment in terms of children's development (fearing they may disturb 'childhood innocence' before it is necessary to do so). Children's accounts do not necessarily support parents' assumptions and many prefer not to talk to parents. A typical (middle class) parental approach is to rely on giving written material to children about sex. However, many parents avoid the tasks suggested as important by their statements that they are waiting for the questions to come from the children and intend to answer them fully at that point. Some use topics that come up at school, on the television, in the newspapers as 'hooks' on which to hang a few facts about sex. But they rarely seem to get down to what the children really want to know about. This in turn raises the question of whether children know what they want to know. Hence if children do not ask the right questions then they are unlikely to receive the answers and explanations they seek.

Parents' own experience of sex education provided to them as children by their parents is important. It works in a variety of ways with respect to its effects on parents' approaches to the sex education of their own children. Some parents clearly repeat their parents' mistakes and omissions while others succeed in acting differently and are able to discuss sex more openly with their children. From their accounts of their own childhood which reflect those of their children, parents testify to the significance of the child's attitude, namely his or her willingness to be 'talked to' about sex. In addition they refer to their own parents' embarrassment and reticence on these matters.

Sex education is discussed by parents and health educators with the benefit of hindsight. It is therefore by definition approached from an adult perspective. Adults perceive the ideal sex educator as someone always available to deal with children's questions and worries, and to clarify points as and when they arise. But, as children, this was not necessarily what parents said they had wanted from their own parents nor do their own children necessarily want this from them. 'Shy' and 'embarrassed' are words which crop up frequently in the interview transcripts to refer to child/parent communication with respect to sex. Adults rarely *ask* children what they want with regard to sex education either in terms of information or mode of communication.

7. Smoking

This chapter examines the smoking habits and attitudes of parents and children. It looks at the influence of a variety of factors upon children's smoking attitudes and practice: for example, household effects including parental and sibling habits, the effects of parental employment, the influence of peers and the impact of parental rules. It identifies different approaches or styles within households with respect to smoking which encompass the role of children as well as parents. Children's reports of their experience of health education with respect to smoking provided by teachers are also discussed.

FACTORS ASSOCIATED WITH PARENTS' SMOKING BEHAVIOUR

We asked the children in the questionnaire survey whether their parents or any other people they lived with smoked. Table 7.1 shows the children's reports of their parents' smoking behaviour by household composition.

Table 7.1   Parental smoking by household composition: questionnaire survey

	Mother and father households %	Mother or father plus step-parent %	Lone mother %
Mother smokes	18	53	30
Don't know	[1]	[1]	[1]
Father smokes	34	56	–
Don't know	[4]	[1]	–
Both smoke	13	40	–
Neither smokes	61	28	69
N	332	43	80

[ ] indicates number not percentage

    Children living in lone-mother households are more likely to have a mother who smokes (30 per cent) compared with those living with two birth parents (18 per cent). However, those living with a step-parent report an even higher incidence of smoking by their mother or stepmother (53 per cent). Thirty-four per cent of fathers in two-parent (birth-parent) households smoke and 56 per cent in step-parent households. Thus, while lone mothers have higher smoking rates than birth mothers in two-parent families, they have lower rates than fathers. Moreover lone-mother *households* are least likely to contain a smoking parent: 30 per cent of lone-mother households are reported to contain smokers compared with 72 per cent of step-parent households and 39 per cent of birth-parent households in which one or both parents smoke. Moreover, 40 per cent of children in step-parent households are exposed to two parents smoking compared with 13 per cent in two-birth-parent households.

Table 7.2 Parents' smoking behaviour by household composition and ethnicity: questionnaire survey

	Mother and father households		Mother or father plus step-parent		Lone mother	
	%	N	%	N	%	N
Asian						
Mother smokes	2	84	0	1	[1]	10
Father smokes	30	87	0	1	–	–
White						
Mother smokes	25	202	62	29	47	40
Father smokes	36	203	60	30	–	–
Black						
Mother smokes	19	31	[4]	10	15	26
Father smokes	26	31	[4]	10	–	–

[ ] indicates number not percentage

Table 7.2 shows marked differences in smoking patterns by ethnicity, particularly for mothers. Whereas 25 per cent of white mothers in two-parent households smoke, only 2 per cent of comparable Asian-origin mothers smoke. Asian-origin fathers are also reported to smoke less than white fathers (30 per cent compared with 36 per cent). Moreover, whereas only 30 per cent of all lone mothers smoke, 47 per cent of white lone mothers are reported to be smokers.

PARENTAL EMPLOYMENT AND SMOKING

There are differences in reported smoking behaviour of parents by parents' employment status. Unemployment increases the likelihood of smoking significantly: among resident fathers, 54 per cent of the non-employed are smokers compared with 28 per cent of fathers in full-time employment and 38 per cent in part-time work. For mothers there are no significant differences. However, more non-employed mothers are smokers compared with those who are employed (28 per cent versus 22 per cent).

Table 7.3 shows the questionnaire survey data for two-parent households (excluding step-parents) and for lone-mother households taking account of household employment patterns. Stepfamilies are excluded since the questionnaire survey contains only 43 of these and this group was not covered in the case studies. At a household level, those two-parent households with neither parent in employment or only one in part-time employment have the highest rate of smoking for fathers (50 per cent), followed by fathers in households where the father is normally the full-time worker and the mother is not employed. Among mothers the highest rate is among lone-mother, non-employed households. The lowest incidence of smoking is found among mothers in two-parent households where both parents are working.

Twelve case study households have a resident parent who is a current smoker: eight fathers and six mothers. In two of these households, both parents smoke. At least one parent in 26 households have never smoked but only seven households have two non-smoking parents who have never smoked. Four of the six smoking mothers work full-time, the remaining two are not employed.

Some parents mention the influence of their employment on their smoking habits.

Table 7.3 Parental smoking by household employment and household composition: questionnaire survey

	Two-parent households				Lone mother households	
	N	mother smokes %	father smokes %	both smoke %	N	mother smokes %
Both working full-time	86	15	17	8	–	–
1 full-time + 1 part-time	106	13	30	8	–	–
1 full-time or 2 part-time	80	25	44	21	25	24
1 part-time or none working	58	24	50	17	55	34

A father working shifts on underground track maintenance, reports an early introduction to smoking but also says that his current smoking is governed by his working environment – the influence of other people who smoke and also the pressures of his job:

> I have always being around people who would smoke all the time. I have tried to give it up but it's very hard to. I have stopped for a week, two weeks at a time but I suppose being working, it's very pressurised . . . All the people smoke, so I am in an environment where everyone smokes.

A mother who smokes at home works in a kitchen all day, an environment which stops her from smoking. She contrasts this with her husband's situation:

> He smokes more than I do, but he can in his job, you see . . . I can't smoke so it's quite easy for me [not to smoke].

Another UK-origin mother working in a hospital says that she became increasingly aware of the hazards and this has led to her giving up smoking. An Asian-origin mother, a non-employed widow who smokes, explains to the interviewer how she came to take up smoking, under the influence of her UK-origin workmates.

> I got a bad habit of smoking, I got a bad habit, twenty years I have been smoking, I can never do that in our village . . . It is because when I started in the factory in Lyon's Maid I had two of my British friends (who smoked).

CHILDREN'S SMOKING BEHAVIOUR

Table 7.4 shows that, in total, 28 per cent of children who answered the questions on smoking (91 per cent) in the questionnaire survey report that they smoke or have tried smoking in the past.

This includes those who say they have tried smoking only once or twice. Only ten children claim to be either occasional or regular smokers (seven occasional and three regular), whilst a further 26 say that they tried smoking in the past. Boys are significantly more likely than girls to say they have done so (35 per cent versus 21 per cent). This is a reversal of the trend found in the study of 16-year-olds where girls were more likely to smoke than boys. National (1992) data for 11-year-olds suggest that 82 per cent of children have never smoked, a figure which is marginally higher

Table 7.4 Children's smoking behaviour by children's sex and ethnic origin: questionnaire survey

	Girls					Boys				
	All %	Asian %	White %	Black %	Other %	All %	Asian %	White %	Black %	Other %
Never smoked	79	91	75	77	[6]	65	73	59	76	[9]
Once or twice	15	5	18	[5]	[2]	27	25	29	20	[4]
Used to smoke	5	–	7	[1]	–	6	–	9	[1]	[1]
Occasionally	[3]	[2]	–	[1]	–	[4]	–	[3]	[1]	–
Regularly	–	–	–	–	–	[3]	[1]	[2]	–	–
N	233	56	135	31	8	254	44	147	46	14

[ ] indicates number not percentage

than our figure for never-smokers; however the figure falls to 69 per cent for 12-year-olds (Church and Summerfield, 1994). Moreover these national data confirm the greater propensity of boys in this age range to smoke in our study. Among the children in the case studies, a quarter say they have tried smoking or are currently doing so – 5/16 boys and 3/18 girls.

Ethnicity is also significant with 17 per cent of Asian-origin children compared with 37 per cent of white respondents admitting to having ever smoked. Again gender is important here with Asian-origin girls least likely to have ever smoked and white boys most likely to have smoked.

With respect to household composition, 74 per cent of children living in two-parent households have never smoked compared with 66 per cent of those living with lone mothers. However, ethnicity is the key issue here since 84 per cent of Asian children and 68 per cent of white children in two-parent families have never tried smoking. Looking only at white children, the differences between those in two-parent households and lone white mother households disappear, 68 per cent of the former and 67 per cent of the latter have never tried smoking. For black children 88 per cent living with two parents and 66 per cent living with lone mothers report never smoking.

CHILDREN'S SMOKING AND PARENTAL SMOKING PATTERNS

Children's smoking is linked to parents' smoking behaviour. Those whose parents are smokers are more likely to have tried smoking than those whose parents do not smoke. The questionnaire survey data reveal that 45 per cent of those whose mothers smoke have tried cigarettes compared with 24 per cent of those whose mothers do not smoke.

Seven of the case study children have tried smoking, two girls and five boys. Both girls are of UK origin and both live in households with smokers present, the mother in one case, an older sibling in the other. Of the five boys who have tried smoking, only one lives in a household in which someone is currently smoking, in this case an older sibling. (Another boy, living with his widowed lone mother reports that his father has been a smoker.)

CHILDREN'S SMOKING AND PARENTAL EMPLOYMENT

There are no statistically significant differences in children's experimentation with smoking by parental employment. Twenty-five per cent of the girls whose mothers work full-time and 21 per cent of those with mothers working part-time have tried smoking. This is compared with 20 per cent of those whose mothers are not employed. For boys, 31 per cent of those with full-time working mothers, 38 per cent of those with part-time working mothers and 36 per cent of those whose mothers do not work report that they have ever tried smoking.

There are differences by mothers' employment status when the mothers' smoking practice is taken into account. Looking only at the group whose mothers do *not* smoke, daughters of full-time employed mothers are more likely to have tried smoking: 20 per cent compared with 12 per cent of those whose mothers work part-time, and 11 per cent of those whose mothers do not work. However, in cases where mothers are smokers, girls whose mothers work full-time are less likely to have tried (39 per cent) compared with 50 per cent of those with part-time employed mothers and 47 per cent of those with non-working mothers.

CHILDREN'S SMOKING AND SIBLING/PEER EXAMPLE

Older siblings appear to be an important influence in the smoking habits of 12-year-olds. In the questionnaire survey, 12 per cent of girls with no older siblings have tried smoking compared with 26 per cent of those with older brothers or sisters. For boys the difference is more significant; 26 per cent with no older siblings have tried smoking compared with 43 per cent of those with older siblings. Of those with older siblings living in the household, 20 per cent (53) report that their siblings smoke. Whilst only 14 per cent of those who never smoked report an older sibling who smokes, 33 per cent of those who have ever smoked report that they have an older sibling who smokes.

The ever-smokers are more likely to have friends who smoke. Only 24 per cent of never-smokers report some or most of their friends as smokers compared with 63 per cent of those who have ever smoked. Only 7 per cent of the non-smokers report that someone has encouraged them to smoke compared with 59 per cent of those who have ever smoked. Boys are significantly more likely to have friends who smoke: 43 per cent of boys and 27 per cent of girls report having smokers as friends.

CHILDREN'S SMOKING INTENTIONS

In the questionnaire survey children were asked a series of questions about what they thought their behaviour would be when they reached the age of 16 with respect to health-related behaviours – smoking, drinking, taking exercise, etc. A 'don't know' category was included in the answers in this section.

Only 14 children responded that they thought that they would be smoking when they were 16 years old. Eleven of these have already tried smoking and all but four live in households where at least one person smokes. There are no significant differences by sex with 77 per cent of girls and 75 per cent of boys saying that they will not be smoking. There are differences by ethnicity with 85 per cent of the Asian-origin children and 81 per cent of the black children anticipating that they will not smoke. This compares with only 73 per cent of the white children. The 'don't know' category forms 20 per cent of the total with Asian-origin and black children least

Table 7.5 Children's response to question 'Do you think you will be a smoker at sixteen': questionnaire survey

	Will smoke		Don't know		Will not smoke		
	%	*n*	%	*n*	%	*n*	*N*
Girls	2	4	21	44	77	162	210
Boys	5	10	20	44	75	164	218
Asian	2	2	12	10	85	68	80
White	3	9	24	61	73	188	258
Black	4	3	14	10	81	56	69
Other	–	0	40	7	60	11	18

likely to be unsure about their future smoking behaviour and almost a quarter (24 per cent) of white children unsure.

There are no significant differences with respect to household composition and employment status of the mother or father. Family position is, however, relevant here, with those who have older siblings significantly more likely to report that they will be smoking or that they are unsure. Those children with no older siblings at home are significantly more likely to report that they will not be smoking (84 per cent) with 1 per cent saying they think they will smoke and 15 per cent not sure. However, of those with older siblings at home, only 71 per cent think that they will not be smoking with 5 per cent reporting that they will and a further 24 per cent unsure.

FAMILY HEALTH AND SMOKING

The negative effects of smoking on health was a common theme among parents and children and often illustrated with specific examples of members of their kin dying from smoking-related diseases. This non-employed lone mother does not smoke and both she and her son are very strongly anti-smoking. The mother's brothers and sisters smoke and she blames her own mother's premature death on smoking:

> If she'd given them up when she first had her first heart attack, then she'd still be here now and she'd have been healthy, walking around . . . I was told if I smoked I'd have a cigarette rammed down my throat – which did frighten the life out of me. When you're 10 and you get told that . . . but my brothers and sisters never took any notice of it, you know. I was the only one that ever did.

Another non-smoking mother talks about her main reasons for being against smoking. She herself smoked in the past but her husband has never smoked and neither of her twin daughters has tried smoking:

> The main reasons, my mother died of cancer and we think that was smoking-related. It is cancer of the oesophagus but it obviously went to the lungs. I think it stems from smoking.

An Asian boy explains his grandfather's ill health in terms of his smoking:

> It's like bad, and people can die from it, they get cancer and things like that. Like my granddad, he's had three heart attacks from smoking, well maybe four, but

he's like still okay now, like. I just don't want that to happen to me or anyone in the family.

CHILDREN'S SMOKING: PARENTAL RULES AND CHILDREN'S VIEWS

In the questionnaire survey, 94 per cent of the children say that their parents have strict rules about smoking, 2 per cent report flexible rules and 4 per cent say that their parents have no rules about smoking. There are no differences by child's sex, ethnicity, presence of older siblings or by the employment status of their mother or father. However, those whose mothers smoke are significantly more likely to report flexible rules than are those whose mothers do not smoke (6 per cent versus 1 per cent). There is no such difference by fathers' smoking habits.

Children were also asked if they thought that it was okay for someone of their age to smoke. Only 2 per cent say that they think it is okay, 93 per cent say that it is not and 5 per cent are undecided. Again there are no differences by sex, ethnicity, the presence of older siblings or by the employment status of the mother or father. There is no significant difference between those whose mothers smoke and those who do not. However, children's views are associated with parental rules. Ninety-six per cent of those who think that it is not okay to smoke (450 out of 467) report strict rules at home whilst only 75 per cent of those who are undecided as to whether it is okay (18 out of 24) do not (report such rules).

Children's normative views are associated with their own smoking behaviour. Almost all the 'never smokers', 336 out of 344 (98 per cent) think that it is not okay compared with 111 out of 133 (83 per cent) of those who have tried smoking. Only three (2 per cent) of the ever-smokers think it is okay compared with four (1 per cent) of the never-smokers. A higher proportion of the ever-smokers, 19 out of 133 (14 per cent), is undecided whether it is okay to smoke compared with only 4 of the 344 (1 per cent) never-smokers.

HOUSEHOLD APPROACHES WITH RESPECT TO SMOKING

Three household approaches or styles with respect to smoking are identified in the case studies:

- Parents are proactive agents who seek to ban smoking in the household and to prevent their children from taking it up.
- Children are proactive agents preventing or stopping their parents smoking.
- Parents and children take a liberal view and adopt a less prescriptive approach to smoking.

Parents as proactive agents

These households adopt a prescriptive approach to smoking; they are against it both in principle and practice. In this group there are 19 households in which none of the parents currently smokes (including seven households where parents have never smoked) and where negative orientations to smoking are largely successful. However, in three households (all Asian-origin) fathers smoke but the general ethos of the family is strongly anti-smoking. A UK-origin household with two employed parents is very anti-smoking and allows no one, not even visitors, to smoke in the house. The mother explains their non-smoking policy in terms of being keen on sport and also notes that it is the children who are particularly anti-smoking:

> We're all very keen on sport, and that's quite incompatible with smoking. Smoking – yes they know that we are horrified, well we just don't like it. We can't stand the smell, plus the health risk.

When talking about his own upbringing, the father claims that his own mother's views on smoking were only coincidental to his own, that he made up his own mind. This argument does not, however, prevent him from being highly prescriptive with his own children:

> I don't think the fact that my mother happened to be of the same opinion is entirely relevant here. There are other things I might not have agreed with her on. One comes to one's own judgement and one practices it, one preaches it. And our children are very aware of this.

The son, however, has already experimented with smoking and is not sure whether he will smoke in the future:

> (*Do you think you'll smoke when you are older?*) Umm. I don't really want to. But yeah, I don't really know at all. (*And why do you say you wouldn't want to?*) My parents wouldn't be very happy. Because Dad got very angry when he found out.

In the Asian-origin households, negative orientations to smoking are integral to cultural mores. Smoking is frowned upon as an immoral habit, particularly by mothers (Brannen *et al.*, 1994). This Asian-origin mother, a non-smoker married to an occasional smoker, describes being surprised about the prevalence of smoking when she first came to England. Her immediate reaction was that it was 'wrong':

> Yeah, actually when I come in this country there was a lot of people smoking that I never see in India, I never see in our culture or families or our neighbour. Nobody else was. I was so surprised when I see even young children, young ladies they are smoking. I ask my husband I say everybody smoke in this country, what's wrong?

Asian-origin families regard smoking in front of elders, the older family members who set and uphold the moral standards of the kin group, as highly disrespectful. Smoking as a health hazard is very much a secondary concern. A father from Pakistan explains that although he himself smokes occasionally, he would never smoke in the presence of his own father or grandfather. He also says that he would not let his son smoke at least as long as he is under his 'command', again ensuring respect from the younger generation for the older generation:

> I don't even smoke in front of him, we have respect . . . (*And do you think [the son] has ever tried a cigarette?*) No, no, he wouldn't touch it. (*Do you think he ever would?*) I doubt it, until 16 he can't, as long as he's in my command, after that it's up to him. (*At 16 you wouldn't mind if he did after that?*) I would mind, I would tell him he wouldn't smoke in front of me, whenever I see him I'd say, if he would do it behind my back that's up to him.

Children as proactive agents

Children as well as parents are significant agents in discouraging smoking in families.

They too mention the negative health effects of smoking but they tend to emphasise its unaesthetic aspects to a greater extent, namely the nasty smell, together with its incompatibility with sports and fitness. An employed mother describes her daughter as anti-smoking because she dislikes the smell:

> She doesn't like me and [the husband] smoking and often moans at us because of the smell or 'Oh, it's getting in my eyes,' and all this sort of thing.

The daughter talks about this rather more fully:

> Because, I know my mum and dad smoke, and I don't like the smell of it sort of thing, and like I find it really hard sometimes in the back of the car . . . I don't like it cos I don't like the idea of having smoke all round and that I would rather be alone . . . I go, 'I hope I don't smoke because you two are getting worse.'

Another mother in a household where both parents smoke reports how 'they get lectures all the time' and how they, the parents, get banished to their bedroom in their flat when they want to smoke. The daughter reports her disgust at their habit but does not regard herself as lecturing her parents:

> I see them smoking and I think, 'Oh! that's disgusting!' . . . they think that's good with me telling them how horrible and disgusting that is. They usually go in their room and smoke.

A boy of UK-origin has older, employed brothers who smoke. He disapproves of his mother smoking and says he has tried to discourage her. He mentions the smell and how incompatible smoking is with being sporty. He also reveals that he has been pressed to smoke on many occasions but appears to have no problem resisting:

> It stinks. It's disgusting, makes your clothes smell. My mum smokes, I don't like it. (*Have you ever tried one?*) No. (*Never? Not even a puff?*) No. (*Has anyone ever offered you one?*) Yes. (*Lots of times?*) Yeah. (*What about when you are older? Do you think you might ever?*) No, 'cos I like to play football.

His lone mother, who works full-time, explains how she refrained from smoking for most of the years of her marriage to a man who did not smoke but, since his departure, she has started again, much to her 12-year-old son's disgust. However, despite her son's negative approach, she is not convinced that he will not smoke one day; her older sons took up smoking despite their earlier protestations. At the same time, she blames herself, suggesting that had she smoked when her elder sons were young, paradoxically they might have been put off starting themselves.

> I don't think he has tried one [cigarette] and he hates the fact that I have started again. (*Really, do you think he ever will smoke when he is older?*) That's hard to say. I thought that about my other children. (*And do they?*) Yeah, they all smoke. Then I thought, that's because I gave up and they didn't know how obnoxious it was.

Children and parents take a liberal view

Some parents and children take a liberal view of smoking. This approach is part and parcel of the liberal philosophy of parenthood by which children are encouraged to develop and make their own choices and decisions in the process of growing up. However, in the questionnaire survey, 94 per cent of children say that their parents have strict rules about smoking. Even so, some parents clearly adopt a relaxed approach, regarding children's experimentation with cigarettes as part of the 'normal process of growing up'. Moreover, some parents and children suggest that children and teenagers will try anything and that if things are forbidden or frowned upon, then they will try them all the more. There is evidently a clear realisation that though parents may wish to take a strong line this may have the opposite effect and encourage children to smoke. A father who smoked himself from the age of 14 until well into his thirties believes that children should be discouraged but not too actively:

> Yes, because it is a habit, but discouraging, um, again it's a very thin line. To say 'you can't and you won't and you mustn't' then they will, won't they?

In the next household, both the mother and father take a liberal view and think that trying to stop children is a waste of energy. Neither parent smokes although the mother used to smoke when she was younger. The father says:

> I personally think smoking is a dirty habit, a waste of money and it's probably not very healthy and it's also not very pleasant for other people. But er, whilst I might express those views to them, if they take it upon themselves they've got the money to smoke, one has to be realistic and say they'll do it and you're just wasting your energy trying to worry about stopping them.

The son has tried smoking but told the interviewer that he dislikes it. He feels that he will not smoke when he is older because he suffers from asthma.

A lone mother who recently stopped smoking relates her 'laid back' reaction when she found her asthmatic daughter experimenting with a cigarette:

> I didn't flip, no no no no. There is no point. I meant I just said I thought it was a very stupid thing to do particularly as she was asthmatic. I asked her if she enjoyed it and she said she didn't. She wanted to see what it was like because I did it. And that made me think ... yeah but it's like anything, you tell someone not to do it and they're bound to turn round and do it. I think you just have to, not badger them but just keep gently reminding them as to why it's not good to smoke. But the more you sort of thrust all the adverse effects of it down their throat they shut off, they don't want to know.

Her daughter also talked about the incident to the interviewer and the reason she gave for smoking – to try it out:

> Just to know what it was like and I thought it was absolutely revolting, and I have like said to myself, I am not going to smoke, but I can't really predict the future, can I?

In another household where both parents smoke, the father took a firm line with his older son, banning him from smoking in the house while smoking himself. However, he now claims that it is inevitable that young people will try to do these things:

> As you and I know, the more you ban something the more kids are going to do it, definitely. If you say you're not going to do that, certain kids are going to try it just to be different ... That's why kids want to drink alcohol and smoke cause they aren't allowed to do it, they're under age, sex under 16 is not allowed so they try it.

If you say no, you're going to push it to the limit . . . I don't see how you can stop kids from getting their hands on cigarettes, there's always going to be a supply.

Although parents may adopt this liberal view, 16 out of 18 girls and 15 of the 16 boys think that children should be discouraged from smoking. Of the remaining children, two girls say they do not have a view whilst a boy, whose parents are strongly anti-smoking, has tried cigarettes but thinks he will not become a smoker. His attitude is a laissez-faire one: children should be left to decide for themselves:

Well, I suppose it's up to them if they smoke. But you just don't hang around with them whilst they do that. Maybe it's their business if they smoke.

CHILDREN'S REPORTS OF SMOKING EDUCATION

Table 7.6 suggests that teachers play only a minimal role in children's smoking education when compared with parents and friends. Whilst 64 per cent of the children say that someone has talked to them about smoking, it is important to note that significant proportions report that no one has spoken to them on this matter. Differences between boys and girls are not marked except with respect to parents; white children report more talk about smoking from parents than do the other ethnic groups. Black children report more talk from friends than do the other groups.

Table 7.6 Sources of smoking education/discussion by gender and ethnicity of children: questionnaire survey

	Girls %	Boys %	Asian %	White %	Black %
Talked about smoking					
with parents	45	36	36	46	23
with teachers	17	12	15	16	8
with friends	22	24	17	23	31
spoken to no one	34	38	41	31	46
N	229	243	98	273	74

The case study parents report considerably more discussion than do the children in their responses in the questionnaire survey. As with conversations about sex education, children acknowledge less interaction while parents perceive more. Only two fathers and two mothers report no conversations about smoking with their children. However, two mothers say that they have talked a lot to their daughters about smoking and one boy has been the recipient of a great deal of talk from both his strongly anti-smoking parents which perhaps explains his own relaxed attitude! All the remaining parents claim to have talked about smoking with their children.

The case studies throw further light on the role of schools in smoking education and suggests greater discussion of the topic in school than at the time of the questionnaire survey. This is not surprising since the interviews took place much later in the school year than the questionnaire. Thirteen out of 18 girls and all 16 boys said that smoking has been talked about at school by teachers. Children report a more informal approach than that used for sex education, with topic work and special assemblies devoted to the issue. One boy mentions an experiment to demonstrate tar deposits in the body as a result of cigarettes.

Many children mention talking to peer groups as an (informal) source of smoking education. In these comments, children suggest some clues as to their liberal approaches explaining that those who experiment with smoking, mainly boys, do so to enhance their personal image; to look 'hard' or 'cool' were the terms they used:

It's normally with their friends. If they smoke, their friends will end up smoking and things like that. It's like trying to be hard and that.

They think that they are hard and it's a hard thing to do.

Well, they think it's cool and they think: 'Everyone else does it, so why shouldn't I?'.

Since male children try cigarettes often to impress their peers, this, in the children's view, creates a difficult challenge for health education. Many are not surprisingly sceptical about the effects of health education on discouraging smoking. A girl says:

Sometimes I think they smoke because they think it's cool and all their friends do it, but some people do it because of the nicotine or whatever's in it. People who think it's cool should just, I don't know, really see pictures of what it can do to you. But you *can't do more* [our emphasis] than show them and tell them and stuff and give them cases of what's happened. And maybe what you can buy instead of cigarette packets.

Other methods of discouraging children from smoking – poems and posters for example – are not expected to cut much ice. A girl with smoking parents reports on anti-smoking activities at school with some cynicism:

We had to do an anti-smoking campaign, which was to put people off smoking and just my luck I was working with someone who did smoke, and we had to do it out in assembly and show our plays or whatever we had done. (*Did people learn new things from that?*) I think they must have paid attention to it, but they didn't really, you know, they listened to it but *they didn't really pay much attention* [our emphasis]. (*Why do you think they didn't pay much attention?*) Cos if you smoke you are not going listen to a couple of kids that are just saying 'Don't smoke, it causes this and this and this' cos they just don't believe it.

This Asian girl favours dramatic health messages but again dismisses their effect:

Just tell them about what it does to you. That you will die more quickly than anyone else. But *I don't think they would listen* anyway.

This latter sentiment is frequently expressed by the children: that it is up to people to make up their own minds, that they are unlikely to take much notice of health education on its own since they are putting their own life at risk anyway which in their view is a personal choice. This girl, like several others, says that she thinks it important not to start smoking in the first place, perhaps echoing the often repeated regret of adults – 'I wish I'd never started':

But he is addicted to it, he can't stop now. So *I don't think you can stop anyone who is smoking now*, but if you can stop the people who aren't smoking it's all right.

A more drastic solution is suggested by one boy, namely that the government should prevent the sales of cigarettes, though he is aware of the unlikelihood of this action because of the vested interests of government and industry:

> Maybe stop selling cigarettes . . . I think that's the best thing you can do is to get rid of them all. The government won't do it because they are the ones who are getting the money. They get money from cigarette firms so they won't stop it. And I think it's a waste of life and also I think it's unfair when you are on trains and London Transport when you have to inhale it without smoking.

While many children are sceptical, some are more optimistic about the effects of smoking education when scare tactics are shown to work:

> Tell them what happens to their bodies when they smoke, 'cos like they'll get sick of it, when they hear that they'll get bad breath, heart disease, lung cancer . . . like the head of year, he smokes and last year he stopped smoking when he saw the assemblies on smoking, he heard about what happened to your heart and everything and he hasn't smoked since.

SUMMARY POINTS

Children are more likely to be exposed to cigarettes in step-parent households (in 40 per cent of which both parents smoke and in 72 per cent at least one parent smokes). Children are least likely to be exposed to smoking parents in lone-mother households (in 30 per cent of which the mother smokes compared with two-birth-parent households in 39 per cent of which there is at least one smoker but in only 13 per cent of which both parents are smokers). Smoking rates of fathers are higher than those of mothers with 34 per cent of fathers smoking in two-birth-parent households and 56 per cent in step-parent households. Smoking is more common among the white parents of UK-origin than in Asian-origin households. Unemployment among fathers also increases the likelihood of smoking but not among mothers. The lowest incidence of smoking is found among mothers in two-parent households where both are in employment. The workplace constitutes a significant context influencing parents, in some cases to engage in smoking and in other cases to desist from it.

Confirming the national picture, over a quarter of children in the questionnaire survey (28 per cent) report having ever tried smoking though the great majority has done so on only one or two occasions. Again confirming national data, boys are significantly more likely to try smoking than girls, which is a reversal of the trend found at 16. Around a quarter of the children interviewed in the case studies have similarly experimented. Like their parents, children of Asian origin are less likely to have tried smoking with Asian-origin girls least likely to do so. Children's smoking is influenced by having older siblings and also by having older siblings who smoke; this is particularly so with respect to male children. Children, boys in particular, who try smoking are also more likely to have friends who smoke. When mothers' smoking practice is taken into account, girls' smoking is differentiated by mothers' employment status, with daughters of full-time employed mothers more likely to have tried smoking if their mothers are non-smokers and less likely if their mothers are smokers (that is, compared with daughters of part-time and non-employed mothers). Three-quarters of children do not expect to smoke when they are 16 but a substantial proportion (24 per cent) says they are unsure.

While the great majority of children report parents applying strict rules about smoking, many parents and children are against taking a prescriptive approach arguing that it will have the opposite of the desired effect, that is it may actually encourage smoking. Children are almost unanimously opposed to smoking. However, if they have tried smoking they are more likely to think it okay to smoke. There is moreover a strong association between those reporting strict parental rules and those children who are opposed to smoking.

Families adopt three different approaches and styles in their response to smoking. In some households, many of Asian origin, parents are proactive in banning smoking and in preventing children from taking it up. This approach is not always successful and where it is clearly unsuccessful may give way to a relaxed attitude. In a second approach, children (rather than parents) are proactive in discouraging smoking at home, an approach which is largely shaped by children's 'disgust' with the unaesthetic aspects of the habit but also with its perceived incompatibility with a sporty lifestyle. Thirdly, parents and children in some households take a liberal view either on the grounds of children's experimentation being a normal part of growing up (a parental view), or on the grounds that prescription would have effects counter to those desired.

Parents and children, especially those of UK origin, have absorbed health messages concerning the negative health consequences of smoking. By contrast, Asian-origin parents regard smoking as infringing moral rather than health norms. In particular they expect members of the younger generation to show 'respect' for the older generation by refraining from smoking.

Despite the apparently prescriptive 'anti' attitudes of children expressed in the questionnaire responses, children and parents are sceptical about the effects of anti-smoking education and campaigns in the case study interviews. Smoking is seen as a personal choice or an individual decision made, according to children's accounts, in order to impress their friends and among boys to give them a 'hard' image. Parental liberalism on smoking appears to be part and parcel of child-rearing approaches which place emphasis on notions of individual choice and the children taking responsibility for their own actions.

8. Children's illness and accidents

In this chapter we examine children's and parents' reports of children's illness and accidents in their first year of secondary school. We consider the extent to which starting secondary school is associated with increased responsibility for the management of illness, taking responsibility for medication, going to the doctor and caring for themselves at home; how children and parents negotiate taking time off school for illness and the pressures on parents in employment against taking time off themselves to look after children.

CHILDREN'S REPORTS OF THEIR ILLNESS

Overall 69 per cent of the children say that they have no problems with illness. Significantly more boys (17 per cent) than girls (10 per cent) report having asthma. However, 8 per cent of girls suffer from other allergies compared with 4 per cent of boys. Eight girls (3 per cent) suffer from headaches but only four boys (1 per cent) mention these. Eleven girls and six boys list skin problems. There are no differences in the incidence of these reported illnesses by ethnicity or parents' employment. In the case studies, seven children say that they suffered in varying degrees of severity with asthma, three with hay fever, and two mention eczema.

CHILDREN'S REPORTS OF ACCIDENTS

Significantly more boys (32 per cent) than girls (24 per cent) report having accidents since they started at secondary school. Most of these accidents involved incidents which occurred at school (57 per cent) while 9 per cent happened in a park or sports centre, 18 per cent at home or in the garden and 8 per cent in the street or on the road. Almost 60 per cent are related to sport or physical exercise. Not surprisingly, since boys are more likely to have taken part in a sport, sport-related accidents are gender-related: 65 per cent of the boys' accidents compared with 46 per cent of the girls' are in this category.

Overall, 68 per cent say that they have sought medical advice or help after the incident, leaving 32 per cent being dealt with informally. Of those who sought professional help, 65 per cent have been to the school nurse, 27 per cent to the doctor and 44 per cent to hospital. Half of those who went to the hospital went straight there, the other half saw either the doctor or the nurse first. There are no significant differences by gender in type of help sought. However, white children are significantly more likely to seek professional assistance than are the Asian children where accidents occur in the home or garden. There is no difference for the accidents which occurred at school or in the street.

In the case studies, five girls report injuries or minor accidents. The three UK-origin girls all attended hospital as a consequence of their injuries. One damaged her knee swimming, resulting in an operation, another fainted while out shopping, hit her head on a counter and was taken to casualty for a check-up. The third was having continuing problems with her knee as a consequence of being tripped at school. Of the two Asian girls, one sprained her ankle and saw the school nurse, the other fell and had first aid from the family. Five boys reported accidents, three sport-related. Two boys, both of Asian origin, took no action, one of whom was still having trouble with his knee a month after the original injury. The third boy's sports injury occurred playing football and resulted in a visit to the doctor. A fourth (UK-origin) boy hurt his wrist falling from his bike and his shoulder while being 'boisterous' at home; both injuries resulted in trips to the hospital. The fifth (UK-origin) boy sustained a broken shoulder falling off his bicycle and, after a complicated operation to set the bone, was in hospital for three weeks. This confirms the lesser likelihood of Asian-origin children seeking professional help when accidents occur.

PARENTS' ACCOUNTS OF CHILDREN'S ILLNESS

Several parents point to their child's first year in secondary school as being one of the worst ever for their children. Some parents report stressful situations at school which led directly to their child having time off, others related illness histories with no school connections. A non-employed mother reports that one of her daughters has had a very difficult year, whilst the twin has had no problems:

> She's had an awful lot of infections . . . I think she had about three weeks out in the year which is quite a lot. If you'd asked me this time last year I would have said they were both very healthy children.

Other parents see clear associations between their child's illness and the problems of settling in at secondary school. This lone mother reports a particularly difficult first year, describing her daughter as 'a disaster on two legs':

> It just seems to be this year everything that could go wrong, has gone wrong. On average she is not unhealthy. This last year I would say has probably been the worst in her twelve years, um, but if it's not been one accident after another or her asthma, it's been something else . . .

This view is endorsed by the daughter in her comment 'I have virtually got everything under the sun'. In fact the daughter was being bullied by some other children in her class. The misery and stress of the situation eventually resulted in her feeling too ill to go to school, rather than talking to her mother about the problems. The daughter says:

> I refused to go to school, because I was getting so fed up with it. It was making me ill. I was making myself sick just to have a day off and then at the end of it when Mum sort of clicked that I was making myself ill, she wanted to know what was wrong, and I couldn't tell her.

The mother recalls how she tried to find out what was wrong and her suspicions that her daughter might be bringing on her asthma attacks deliberately:

> I kept saying, is there anything worrying you, no no . . . it was doing her in and it was certainly doing me in watching her not being able to breathe and giving her Ventolin and the doctor had said these are real, she's having these attacks and they're real . . . I started to notice that when I said 'Obviously you can't go to school, I'll take you to Nanny's', she would get better by the time I would get round to my mother's.

CHILDREN'S RESPONSIBILITY FOR MEDICATION

More boys (11 per cent) than girls (8 per cent) report that they help themselves to tablets or medicines. Significantly more girls (32 per cent) than boys (23 per cent) were given tablets by their parents. Around half the children (51 per cent of the boys and 48 per cent of the girls) asked their parents for medicines but 15 per cent of boys and 12 per cent of girls said that they never took any medication at all. Significant differences are found with respect to ethnicity with 38 per cent of Asian-origin children reporting that they are given medication by parents compared with 28 per cent of white children. However, white children are more likely to ask their parents for medication compared with Asian-origin children (55 per cent versus 42 per cent).

Case study parents stress the importance of self-responsibility for routine medication whilst others are not yet ready to allow their child full responsibility. One father reports that his son would 'probably be insulted' if they gave him any medicine, unless he was too sick to get it for himself. This contrasts with another father's view of 'never leave it to children', because 'medicines are very dangerous and should be kept out of reach'.

Children's responsibility for medication varies according to the type of illness. With asthma and eczema, children may have considerable responsibility for their medication. The parents of asthmatic children themselves make the distinction between different medications. This mother describes how she supervises one aspect of her daughter's asthma medication, lets her administer another and discusses the taking of tablets for other conditions:

> The Becotide, she takes morning and night and I watch her do that, I mean I don't administer it. I just watch her do it. The Ventolin she administers herself; if she has a headache or anything then she gets the paracetamol, Hedex and she tells me, she comes and says to me 'I've got a headache' and I say to her 'Take a paracetamol'. She knows what the dosage is and she doesn't go beyond that and I watch her take it.

The next father explains why it is important that his 12-year-old son *learns* to take responsibility for his asthma treatment since he is likely to have the condition for the rest of his life:

> He knows when to take it and it's for him to, basically, it's a benefit to him if he takes it. He doesn't always take it and then gets an asthma attack. One day he'll realise that by taking it, he'll not get asthma attacks . . . he's 12, he's got to learn to . . . it could be potentially a condition that he's got for the rest of his life and he has to start getting used to taking whatever treatment he needs to control it.

A mother encourages her son to deal with the routine application of cream for his eczema:

> I have been trying to get him to take a little bit more responsibility because it's something he can easily apply. He has got his cream and he knows when to apply it but invariably he comes to me and asks me to put it on anyway.

This father of a healthy daughter with no recurrent illnesses stresses his daughter's capability with respect to administering her own medication:

> She's of an age where she knows if she's got medicine to take, if it's three times or whatever. We ask 'Have you taken them?' She would be expected to know, she's

at the age if she needs something she'll say . . . So we know what she's doing, she wouldn't have an extra dosage by mistake. She's quite capable.

The above cases contrast with parents who do not devolve responsibility to children. In some the children rarely take medicine. An Asian-origin mother supervises the giving of medicine to her daughter, and allocates control in the context of the house practice concerning her daughter's access to other household consumables:

> Before she takes it she will ask me. She won't touch anything in the house. It is not the rule, but it is her habit. Even if she wants to eat or have a glass of coke she will ask me 'Mum can I have it?' She won't just go and help herself. So that way I know what she is up to.

CHILDREN'S CONSULTATION WITH MEDICAL SERVICES

Most children say that they have visited their GP in the past six months: 40 per cent have been once or twice, 22 per cent three or four times and 17 per cent have been more frequently. Twenty-one per cent have not been to see their doctor. There are no differences by sex or ethnicity, nor by mothers' or fathers' employment.

Those assessing their health as 'not good' have made more visits to the doctor than those who say that their health is 'good'; or 'fairly good'; 36 per cent of those with the 'not good' health have been five or more times compared with only 13 per cent of those with good health. However, similar proportions of both groups, 22 per cent of those with good health and 21 per cent of those with the not good health, have not been to their doctor at all. Not surprisingly, children reporting an illness or recurrent condition are more likely to have visited the doctor, for example only six out of 74 (8 per cent) reported asthma sufferers had *not* been to the doctor during the six-month period.

Very few children say that they go in to see the doctor on their own (2 per cent). For the majority (78 per cent), they are usually accompanied by their mother, 13 per cent by their father and 5 per cent by some other adult. There are some differences by the frequency of visits, so that those who have been only once or twice are more likely to be accompanied than those who have been five or more times (81 per cent versus 72 per cent). Five per cent of boys say that they have at some time been to see the doctor on their own compared with 2 per cent of girls.

Only two case study children report going to the doctor alone. In one case a mother of Asian origin explains that her son went to the doctor several times that year, sometimes she went with him, sometimes he went alone. However, the doctor's surgery was only two doors away from their home. A UK-origin girl finds her unaccompanied visits less than satisfactory, however, and would prefer to have her mother with her to act as intermediary or interpreter:

> Normally I would go by myself or my [older] brother would have to go the same time as me . . . you can't understand what he says. You don't know what he is saying, and if he tells you to say something to the chemist you don't know what he has told you. So, you say pardon and he will say it again and you don't understand again and he will think you are deaf if you ask him to say it again.

A quarter of children in the questionnaire survey (25 per cent) say that, on their last visit, the doctor spoke mainly to the adult accompanying them and 55 per cent say that the doctor spoke to both of them equally. Only 20 per cent say that the doctor spoke mainly to them. There are no differences by sex or ethnicity. Over half the children (55 per cent) think that the doctor should talk to them directly.

CHILDREN'S TIME OFF SCHOOL FOR ILLNESS

A third of the children in the questionnaire survey had taken no time off school through ill health since they started secondary school; 38 per cent were off for between one and three days, 15 per cent between four and six days and 14 per cent for more than seven days.

There are no significant differences by sex, ethnicity or the presence or absence of older or younger siblings at home. However, there are differences between children living with both their parents and those living with their lone mother; 37 per cent of the former but only 23 per cent of the latter had no days off, and 25 per cent of those with lone mothers but 12 per cent of those with both parents had seven or more days off. Differences according to mothers' employment are discussed below.

In the case studies, only three children had more than a few days off. Several children express pride at their good school-attendance record. One Asian-origin boy had no time off school, another only half a day; two girls were out of school only for regular visits to the orthodontist. Most had only one or two days off during the year, mainly for colds, sore throats, headaches or stomach upsets.

TIME OFF SCHOOL: CHILDREN'S NEGOTIATIONS AND STRATEGIES

Children participate in negotiations concerning time off although parents may ultimately make the decisions. Only one case study child reports that the decision to take time off school was his own and three describe it as a joint decision with their mothers. The Asian-origin boy who sees the decision as being his, describes how he had a day off when he was running a temperature. He sees his mother's readiness to let him stay home as a consequence of her *trust* in him:

> I said to my mum that I'm getting a bit hot and that lot, and she said 'Do you want to stay off, at home?' Like she lets us choose, cos she knows like we go to school and she knows that. We won't say 'No, we don't want to go to school', cos we just go.

Her son's view that his mother trusts his judgement is confirmed in his mother's interview when she tells the interviewer about her son's good attendance record at school for which he was given a certificate, and that he dislikes staying home.

Where the decision about staying home is made by the parent, that parent is overwhelmingly the mother. One father with twin daughters admits that his wife, decides: 'because I'm gone in the morning anyway'. She makes the decision and any necessary arrangements. One boy explains that his (non-working) mother rather than his father took the decision partly because his father was usually at work but also because 'mum really knows when I am ill and when I am faking'.

'Faking' is mentioned by several children as a strategy to avoid going to school. Parents are aware of this strategy and indeed some parents seem to be particularly on the look out for this sort of behaviour. Indeed the start of secondary school may constitute a significant trigger for such behaviour if children find coping with the change difficult. Few of this age group of children have mastered the art of 'bunking off' and being ill is probably the only strategy available to them to avoid unpleasant experiences. This father describes the firm line he takes with his children about being off school and 'faking' illness:

Their mother being a nurse, they're not very successful at kidding her. Number one son got a shock when I had to collect him one day from school on a Friday and in the evening he said well he'd get ready to go off on some scout activity at the weekend that had been arranged for months, to which I said 'Oh no you won't. You're ill today, you're grounded'. And that's a lesson that all three of them absorbed.

However, parents can be over-sensitive to the possibility of their children faking illness. A girl describes with some indignation how she was wrongly accused of faking and sent to school by her full-time employed mother when she was 'really ill':

One time I felt quite ill and my mum said 'Oh no, you're faking it again, you have been faking it all week, haven't you?' I said 'No I haven't been faking it all week,' so I went to school and I got sent home.

At least two mothers admit colluding to some extent with their sons' dubious illness claims. One allowed her son to stay home from school even though she hints that he was 'not really ill'. She was aware that he was finding the transition to secondary school difficult:

One or two minor things, a day here, a day there, sore throat or whatever. And in the early days I think that was because, it was around school issues and there were a couple of times actually I didn't think he was ill. I allowed him to stay at home and made him use that time to catch up on homework or something. Because I was trying to give him time to put himself right.

The boy acknowledges that his mother allowed him this freedom. In the interview he talks about the problems he had settling into his new school:

I used to get angry with the teachers, so my mum used to keep me off ... and that's when I was getting into a lot of trouble at school, shouting at the teachers.

Subsequently he fell off his bicycle and was in hospital for several weeks. He describes in his interview a process of transformation taking place in his character since his accident although he does not explicitly link the two together. He describes a profound alteration in his attitude at school and radical changes in the crowd he mixes with there.

MOTHERS' EMPLOYMENT AND CHILDREN'S ILLNESS

Table 8.1 shows that children of full-time employed mothers have had less time off school than those whose mothers were not in work (36 per cent versus 26 per cent). Also, 25 per cent of those with mothers in full-time employment had four or more days off compared with 35 per cent of those whose mothers were at home. There are no differences in taking time off school through illness between those whose mothers work part-time and those who work full-time.

Researchers argue, at least with respect to younger children, that children with significant ill health are less likely to have mothers who are employed (Hewison and Dowswell, 1994). Mothers fear that taking time off when their child is ill will raise problems and therefore defer their re-entry into the labour market.

Of the three children in the case studies who had more than two weeks off through

Table 8.1 Children's days off school for illness: questionnaire survey

Days off school	Mother works full-time %	Mother works part-time %	Mother not working %
None	36	38	26
1–3 days	39	34	39
4–6 days	13	13	18
7 or more days	12	14	17
N	171	174	168

ill health during their first year at secondary school, one had a non-working mother, the other two had mothers in full-time employment.

For employed mothers, the sick child raises two problems. Firstly restoring the child to good health and secondly the care of the child whilst it is ill. Asked who looked after them last time they had time off school because of illness, only a small proportion (14 per cent) of the children say in the questionnaire survey that they looked after themselves. Most (65 per cent) were looked after by their mothers, 5 per cent were cared for by their fathers and 16 per cent by some other carer. There are significant differences by sex: 19 per cent of boys but only 7 per cent of girls report that they looked after themselves last time they were off school sick.

Table 8.2 Care arrangements for sick children: questionnaire survey

Carer	Mother works full-time %	Mother works part-time %	Mother not working %
Child looked after self	25	12	5
Mother	43	65	85
Father	6	6	4
Other person	26	17	6
N	119	121	136

Table 8.2 shows that mothers' employment is significant with respect to who cares for the sick child. Whereas 25 per cent of those with mothers working full-time look after themselves, only 12 per cent of those whose mothers work part-time say this, as do only 5 per cent of those with non-employed mothers. For those with full-time employed mothers, 43 per cent were looked after by their mother, 6 per cent by their father and 26 per cent by another adult. Fathers' involvement is not influenced by mothers' employment status.

For employed mothers, the illness of their secondary-school children can give rise to great anxiety. The differences with respect to children of full-time employed mothers having less time off school through illness compared with those whose mothers are at home may be a reflection of the firmer line being taken by employed mothers:

He may have had an odd day off with a cold, but I must admit one thing with working, unless they have got a temperature, then they go to school.

Another mother whose daughter has been off a lot was very conscious of the risk of losing her job if she had to keep taking time off to look after her daughter. As a lone mother she bears most of the responsibility for care and does involve her ex-husband, the girl's father:

> I saw him down the road and I said to him 'Look, she's your daughter as well, you've got to get involved in this and I'm going to lose my job as well because I keep having to have time off of work.' And whilst they're very good and understanding, there's only so much an employer is going to put up with.

Whilst the issues of care are clear-cut at younger ages – someone has to care for the child – by the time children are at secondary school more flexible arrangements can be considered. Employed mothers stress the need to make the right decision about whether to send the child to school or not. If the child stays home they must decide whether supervision is required and if so make arrangements for care, either by staying off work themselves or finding another carer. If they send a sick child to school, and this is the wrong decision, then they risk censure from others, especially teachers, and from the children themselves. They risk being considered hard-hearted or selfishly putting their jobs before their children.

The fact that the child may be considered 'old enough' to be left alone at least for part of the time has to be set against the pressures of another tier of decision-making. In some cases, children may be considered 'old enough', i.e. well-enough behaved, for the mothers to take them with them to work. Such options are also dependent upon the nature of the mothers' occupations and their workplaces.

This working mother, a full-time college lecturer, balances the option of taking her son with her against the alternative scenario of being called away from work if her son's condition deteriorates:

> Partly because it [the condition] might get worse, rather than because it was awful at the time, I'd take him with me. I did that once for an examiners' meeting. You can't miss examiners' meetings and I took him in because he might have got sick again and he might not. And if I had been called out it would have been worse than having him (at work). So he sat in my room with crisps and played computer games.

Mothers describe mixed strategies, leaving their child at home alone for part of the time, arranging care or staying home from work, or taking the child with them. A secretary describes one day leaving her son alone and the next day bringing him to work. Significantly this mother also works in a medical environment which may be more sympathetic to children and working mothers' responsibilities:

> I phoned them at work and said I didn't want to leave him on his own 'Could he come with me?' And it was fine, I got him some comics and he sat at an empty desk.

Several mothers report the great lengths they have gone to in order to cope with both work and their sick children – in the following cases working at home or in the case of the district nurse, dropping in on her rounds to see her sick child:

> If they were ill, I could come home, bring books home and do organisational things from home. My office would phone me here and I'd have telephone discussions from home. So for short periods of time I could accommodate that. I am lucky as with my job I can nip in and out during the day in between patients, and you know keep an eye on them.

Mothers making the decisions about children's fitness for school report clearly developed guidelines in relation to the illness symptoms and diagnosis: if the illness is clearly defined and its course totally predictable then the child may often be left alone but if the symptoms are less clear and the outcome is not easily foreseen, then supervision is required. A lone mother who is a full-time secretary explains her decision in terms of the particular illnesses. She would take time off for 'vomiting or anything like that' but not necessarily for a sprained ankle; in the latter case she would adopt a mixed strategy:

> ... if she had sprained her ankle or hurt her leg and it was a question of me having half a day and leaving her for the rest of the day sitting on the chair with her leg up, that's one thing, but when she is sick, something I am not quite sure about, I take time off.

> If they were very ill, if their temperatures were high and they were not doing well then I wouldn't leave them. But if they were groggily watching TV on the sofa then I would leave them for a couple of hours.

SUMMARY POINTS

Illness, as reported by children, is a significant feature of children's first year at secondary school. Allergies, particularly asthma, are common among 12-year-olds. Similarly, accidents are common, with boys more likely to report accidents especially related to sport or physical activity. Over half of accidents occur at school with one-third resulting in hospital attendance. White children are more likely to seek professional assistance after accidents compared with Asian-origin children. Parents also report a considerable amount of children's illness in their first year at secondary school, in some cases connecting it to the transition to secondary school and problems of settling in, including bullying and being bullied. Both parents' and children's accounts suggest that claiming, and in some cases feigning, illness constitutes a strategy whereby children unhappy with secondary school avoid attendance.

Most 12-year-olds do not take responsibility for medication, with the exception of those who are on regular and frequent medication for chronic conditions, notably asthma and eczema. Even with respect to the latter condition, parents may monitor some aspects of the medication and give children total responsibility for other aspects of it. Gender of child and ethnicity are also significant, with girls and Asian-origin children less likely to self-administer medication.

The great majority of children have visited their GP since the start of secondary school but most are accompanied (by their mothers). One-quarter of children say that the last time they visited the GP, the GP did not address them directly. Over half think that the GP ought to speak to them. Not surprisingly, those who go to the GP more frequently are more likely to report that the GP addresses them directly.

Two-thirds of children had some time off school since the start of their first year in secondary school. Those whose mothers are employed are significantly less likely to have had time off. Only a small proportion of children report looking after themselves when they had time off school for illness (14 per cent). However, 25 per cent of those with full-time employed mothers looked after themselves last time they had time off ill. This compares with only 5 per cent of those with non-working mothers.

While mothers were the principal persons to decide if children should stay away from school because of illness, children are actively involved in these negotiations.

As already noted, children make illness claims which may or may not be legitimate in their own terms or those of their parents. Children are highly attuned to the distinctions between legitimate and non-legitimate reasons for staying off school, with some emphasising the trust that their mothers have in them and others complaining that their claims are not taken seriously. In some instances children themselves admit to feigning illness in the context of having problems at school.

Mothers try to balance the needs of their sick children for care against other demands on their time. The issue is especially significant for employed mothers. The fact that few children look after themselves is reflected in the variety of strategies mothers adopt with respect to their care. These strategies do not necessarily mean, however, that mothers simply take time off work. Some adopt flexible strategies such as leaving their children alone for part of the time, taking time off for part of the time, and/or working from home some of the time. A few mothers are employed in workplaces which allow or are sympathetic to mothers bringing their children into work on odd occasions. These decisions are contingent on the nature of mothers' jobs, the attitudes of their employers and the proximity of their workplaces. Mothers also take account of the nature of children's illnesses, setting themselves guidelines for conditions under which they allow children to be responsible for themselves when they are ill.

References

Balding, J. (1993) *Young People in 1992*. Exeter: Schools Health Education Unit.

Brannen, J., Dodd, K., Oakley, A., and Storey, P. (1994) *Young People, Health and Family Life*. Buckingham: Open University Press.

Brannen, J., Meszaros, G., Moss, P. and Poland, G. (1994b) *Employment and Family Life: a Review of Research in the UK (1980–1994)*, Research Series No. 41. London: Employment Department.

Brannen, J. (1995) 'Young people and their contribution to household work', *Sociology*, **19**(2), 317–38.

Bridgwood, A. and Savage, P. (1993) *General Household Survey 1991*. London: HMSO.

Church, J. and Summerfield, C. (eds) (1994) *Social Focus on Children*, London: HMSO.

Gregg, P. and Wadsworth, J. (1995) *More Work in Fewer Households?* In J. Hills (ed), *New Inequalities*. Cambridge: Cambridge University Press.

Health Education Authority (1992) *Tomorrow's Young Adults: 9–15-year-olds look at Alcohol, Drugs, Exercise and Smoking*. London: Health Education Authority.

Hewison, J. and Dowswell, T. (1994) *Child Health Care and the Working Mother: the Juggling Act*. London: Chapman & Hall.

Kirk, D. and Tinning, R. (1994) 'Embodied self-identity, healthy lifestyles and school physical education', *Sociology of Health and Illness*, **16**(5), 600–25.

Martin, J. and Roberts, C. (1984) *Women and Employment: a Lifetime Perspective*. The Report of the 1980 DE/OPCS Women and Employment Survey. London: HMSO.

Smyth, M. and Browne, F. (1992) *General Household Survey 1990*. London: HMSO.

Solberg, A. (1996) 'The challenge in child research: from being to doing' in Brannen, J. and O'Brien, M. (eds) *Children in Families: Research and Policy*. London: The Falmer Press.

Thomas, M., Goddard, E., Hickman, M. and Hunter, P. (1994) *General Household Survey 1992*. London: HMSO.

Woodroffe, C., Glickman, M., Barker, M. and Power, C. (1993) *Children, Teenagers and Health: the Key Data*. Buckingham: Open University Press.

HEA Family Health Research Programme – Report Series
The other four titles in this series can be ordered through Marston Book Services, telephone 01235 465565.